Type 2
Diabetes Cookbook
for Beginners

2000+Days of Super Easy, Tasty, Low-Sugar & Low-Carbs Recipes with Color Pictures and a 30-Day Meal Plan.

Live Healthier, Cook Deliciously!

By Abby Becker

Friendly Disclaimer

Dear Reader, We're delighted you've chosen this cookbook. It's filled with recipes we believe you'll enjoy. Just a friendly reminder—while we've made every effort to offer you excellent tips and recipes to assist in managing Type 2 Diabetes, this book is not a substitute for medical advice. It's important to consult with your healthcare provider about your diet, particularly if you have specific health considerations. Our recipes are designed to inspire you and bring a bit of joy to your culinary endeavors. Here's to creating meals that not only taste great but also contribute to your well-being! Please remember, that the path to managing diabetes is highly individual. What works for one may not work for all. Therefore, treat this book as a companion on your journey, always paying attention to your body and the advice of your healthcare team. Let's embark on this flavorful adventure together!

Abby Becker

Table of Contents

Introduction

Welcome, dear readers! If you find yourself holding this book, you've likely already encountered the diagnosis of "Diabetes." For those who stumbled upon it by chance or out of curiosity, I urge you not to stop reading and pay attention to what's inside. Adhering to the dietary rules outlined in this book can significantly increase the chances that diabetes will never touch you personally.

None of us are ever truly prepared for it to hit. It always comes unexpectedly, like thunder out of a clear sky. In my life, it happened twice. The first time, "Type 2 Diabetes" was diagnosed in my mother at 55 years old. Later on, my twelve-year-old son was diagnosed with "Type 1 Diabetes". Therefore, I fully understand the emotional turmoil one faces when suddenly finding out that your life will never be the same. The good news is that after going through all stages of acceptance and applying certain diligence and adherence to some not-so-unattainable rules, you can learn to live a fulfilling, complete, happy, and long life without the anguish of self-restriction despite diabetes. I aim to help you on this journey not just as a theorist but as a practitioner, considering my own experience, mistakes, and the conclusions drawn from them.

What is Diabetes?

Seasoned readers can confidently skip these chapters and move directly to the recipes and preparation of tasty, healthy, and beautiful dishes for all life occasions - from everyday meals to festive events. Yet, revisiting the basics is never amiss (imagine a winking emoji here).

So, **diabetes** is a chronic condition leading to disruptions in the metabolism of carbohydrates, proteins, and fats in the body, resulting in blood glucose levels rising above normal. Glucose is the primary energy source for our body's cells, and insulin—a hormone produced by the pancreas—is required for its absorption. In diabetes, the process of glucose absorption is disrupted due to a lack of insulin or reduced cell sensitivity to it, leading to various complications and potentially long-term adverse health consequences, including damage to vessels, nerves, heart, eyes, and kidneys.

It's essential to clarify that diabetes comprises several diseases with similar symptoms but different causes and treatment approaches.

Type 1 Diabetes typically occurs in children, adolescents, and young adults. This category of the disease is related to the destruction of beta cells in the pancreas that produce insulin. Essentially, insulin completely disappears from the body's internal environment, resulting in cells being unable to absorb sugar and remaining without an energy source. This disease may manifest following viral infections, significant stress, hormonal changes in the body, failures in the immune system's function, and less commonly—due to genetic predisposition. The exact causes of Type 1 Diabetes remain largely unknown.

Type 2 Diabetes, accounting for about 90% of all diabetes cases and often referred to as the disease of civilization, mainly occurs in people over 40 years old and is directly linked to lifestyle factors such as physical inactivity, excess weight, and unhealthy eating habits. In this case, the pancreas may function properly, and there might be enough insulin in the body, but the cells lose their ability to recognize it. A fitting comparison is a car whose trunk is filled with fuel canisters, but the fuel can't get into the locked tank.

Gestational Diabetes can develop during pregnancy and usually resolves after childbirth. However, it increases the risk of developing Type 2 Diabetes in women in the future.

Symptoms You Can't Ignore

The symptoms of diabetes can vary depending on the level of blood sugar increase. Some individuals, especially those with Type 2 Diabetes, may not initially notice significant changes.

Here are the main signs to watch for:

- **Frequent urination and thirst**: High blood sugar levels force the kidneys to work harder to filter and absorb its excess. When the kidneys can't keep up, the excess sugar is excreted in the urine, pulling fluids from tissues, leading to dehydration and a feeling of thirst.
- **Constant hunger and unexplained weight loss**: The lack of ability to process glucose into energy forces the body to seek alternative sources of fuel, leading to the breakdown of muscle tissue and fat stores.
- **Tendency towards fatigue**: Lack of energy due to poor glucose absorption can cause fatigue and a feeling of constant tiredness.
- **Blurred vision**: High blood sugar levels can pull fluid from the lens of the eye, affecting your ability to focus.
- **Slow healing of wounds, skin infections, and itching**: Excess sugar in the blood can impair the body's healing ability and worsen its natural defense against infections, especially on the skin and mucous membranes.
- **Tingling or numbness in the hands and feet**: High blood sugar levels can damage nerves, causing these sensations.

If you or someone close to you notices any of the symptoms listed, it's crucial to see a doctor immediately. The healthcare professional can order the necessary tests (typically, a blood sugar test and a glycated hemoglobin test) to check your blood glucose levels and either confirm or rule out diabetes.

Causes of the Disease. The Scope of the Problem

By 2023, the global diabetes population neared 540 million. In the US, 38.4 million people suffer from diabetes, accounting for 11.6% of the population. On average, diabetes is diagnosed in one more person worldwide every five seconds, 90% of which are type 2 diabetes cases.

Type 1 diabetes is an autoimmune disease, meaning the body's immune system, which normally protects us from infections, mistakenly attacks and destroys the insulin-producing beta cells in the pancreas. The exact causes of this autoimmune reaction are still unknown.

Contrastingly, type 2 diabetes is directly linked to modern lifestyle choices, characterized by sedentary habits, minimal physical activity, abundant and high-calorie food intake, increased portion sizes, and a diet high in unhealthy fats, quick carbs, refined products, widespread fast food consumption, and a significantly reduced intake of vegetables, fruits, whole grains, and greens. This combination of factors creates conditions where the body becomes less sensitive to insulin, leading to the development of type 2 diabetes.

Type 2 diabetes is often referred to as a scourge of civilization, and its prevalence has reached pandemic proportions. Given its rapidly growing prevalence and serious public health implications, raising awareness about the disease not only helps those living with diabetes manage their condition more effectively but is also crucial for society at large to understand the risks of developing diabetes and to implement preventive measures.

Treating Diabetes. The Role of Diet in Diabetes Management

Despite advancements in modern medicine, it's currently impossible to cure type 1 diabetes fully. The destruction of insulin-producing cells in this condition is considered irreversible, so treatment focuses on replacing pancreatic function through insulin therapy and preventing typical diabetes complications. However, following a special balanced diet is also critical as it helps avoid sudden fluctuations in blood sugar levels. Maintaining a sufficient level of physical activity reduces insulin requirements.

The treatment of type 2 diabetes involves a combination of lifestyle changes and medication. Often, reaching the targeted blood sugar levels can only be achieved through diet and exercise. Without dietary adherence, other diabetes treatments and complication management methods are less likely to be successful.

Why is food so important?

In diabetes, the primary goal is to maintain healthy blood sugar levels. The food you consume daily directly impacts this level. Making informed food choices and understanding how different types of food affect your body can help you control the disease and maintain a healthy lifestyle.

Carbohydrates

Carbohydrates, along with proteins and fats, are one of the three main macronutrients in our diet. They serve as the primary energy source for our bodies and play a crucial role in the functioning of the brain, muscles, and other systems. Based on their chemical structure and digestion rate, carbohydrates are categorized into two main types: simple and complex.

Simple carbohydrates consist of one or two sugar molecules and are quickly digested and absorbed by the body, leading to a rapid increase in blood glucose levels. They include monosaccharides (single sugar molecules) such as glucose, fructose, galactose, and disaccharides (two sugar molecules) like sucrose (table sugar), lactose (milk sugar), and maltose (malt sugar). Simple carbohydrates are found in fruits, dairy products, honey, syrups, and added sugars prevalent in processed foods and sweetened drinks.

Complex carbohydrates, composed of three or more sugar molecules linked together, digest slower, providing a more gradual and sustained energy source. They are found in whole grain products, legumes, vegetables, and some fruits. Complex carbs are also rich in nutrients and fiber, which promotes digestive system health and helps regulate blood glucose levels.

The glycemic index (GI) measures how food products raise blood glucose levels. High-GI foods cause rapid spikes in blood sugar, while low-GI foods result in a slow, gradual increase.

Choosing the right carbohydrates is key to maintaining health and managing weight. Consuming large amounts of simple carbohydrates with high added sugar content contributes to obesity, type 2 diabetes, heart diseases, and other health issues. Conversely, incorporating complex carbohydrates with a low glycemic index into your diet helps sustain fullness, stable energy levels, and healthy digestion. For optimal health and effective weight and blood sugar level management, focus on consuming complex carbohydrates, especially those rich in fiber. Fiber not only aids in normalizing digestive processes and enhancing satiety but also helps slowly increase blood sugar levels after meals, which is crucial for individuals with type 2 diabetes.

Incorporating More Complex Carbohydrates into Your Diet

1. **Choose whole-grain products**: Substitute white bread, rice, and pasta with their whole-grain counterparts, such as whole-grain bread, brown rice, quinoa, buckwheat, and other whole grains.
2. **Eat more vegetables**: Particularly important is the consumption of vegetables low in carbohydrates but high in fiber and nutrients. Fruits are also beneficial, though their carb content should be considered regarding blood sugar impact.
3. **Include legumes in your diet**: Lentils, beans, peas, and chickpeas are rich in fiber and protein, making them an excellent choice for balanced nutrition. 4. Avoid added sugars: Limit your intake of products with high added sugar content, such as sweetened beverages, candies, and baked goods. Carefully read product labels, as added sugars can be listed under various names.
5. **Plan your meals**: Planning your meals for the week ahead can help you make healthier food choices and avoid impulsive consumption of unhealthy foods.

Proteins

Proteins also play a vital role in nutrition for people with type 2 diabetes, not just in maintaining and repairing body tissues but also in managing blood glucose levels. For those with type 2 diabetes, where managing glucose is a key aspect of overall health, proteins become an especially important dietary component for several reasons:

1. **Minimal impact on blood glucose**: Unlike carbohydrates, proteins have a minimal direct effect on blood glucose levels, making them an ideal choice for stabilizing blood sugar. Consuming proteins along with carbohydrates can help slow the absorption of sugar into the bloodstream, preventing sharp glucose spikes after meals.
2. **Satiety and weight control**: Proteins promote a lasting sense of fullness, which can help manage appetite and overall calorie intake. This is particularly crucial for individuals with type 2 diabetes, as maintaining a healthy weight is a key factor in managing the condition and reducing the risk of diabetes-related complications.
3. **Muscle mass maintenance**: Proteins are the building blocks for muscles. Keeping a healthy muscle mass is important for overall health and can help improve metabolism, which in turn supports weight control and enhances insulin sensitivity.

Protein Sources

When choosing protein sources, it's advisable to opt for lean proteins to minimize intake of saturated fats, which can increase the risk of cardiovascular diseases. Good protein sources include lean meats (chicken, turkey), fish, especially fatty types like salmon rich in omega-3 fatty acids, legumes (beans, lentils, chickpeas), nuts and seeds, low-fat dairy products (but not fat-free), tofu, and other soy products.

Fats

Fats are another crucial component of nutrition for everyone, including those with type 2 diabetes. They serve as an energy source and assist in the absorption of fat-soluble vitamins (A, D, E, K) and the maintenance of cell membrane health. However, not all fats are equally beneficial.

Types of Fats

- **Saturated fats** are usually solid at room temperature and found in animal products, such as meat and dairy, as well as some tropical oils (coconut and palm oil). Studies show that excessive intake of saturated fats can raise "bad" LDL cholesterol levels in the blood, increasing the risk of heart disease.

- **Trans fats** are mainly formed during the hydrogenation of vegetable oils and can be present in margarine, processed foods, and some types of baked goods. Trans fats are also linked to an increased risk of heart disease and should be limited as much as possible.
- **Unsaturated fats** are liquid at room temperature and include monounsaturated and polyunsaturated fats. They are found in vegetable oils (olive, sunflower, corn), nuts, seeds, and fatty fish. Unsaturated fats help reduce the risk of heart disease and can improve blood glucose control in type 2 diabetes.

Making the right fat choices can aid in managing type 2 diabetes and reduce the risk of related complications. Incorporating unsaturated fats into your diet while limiting saturated and trans fats supports heart health and may improve insulin sensitivity. Omega-3 fatty acids, particularly those found in fatty fish, provide additional benefits by reducing inflammation and improving blood lipid profiles.

Fat Consumption Recommendations

- Aim for moderate fat intake, as fats are high in calories and can lead to weight gain if consumed excessively.
- Choose foods high in unsaturated fats and limit saturated and trans-fat intake. This not only improves blood cholesterol levels but also contributes to more effective diabetes management.
- Include more fatty fish in your diet, such as salmon, mackerel, and sardines, which are sources of omega-3 fatty acids. It's recommended to eat fatty fish at least twice a week.
- Use plant oils, such as olive, avocado, and sunflower oil, for cooking and salad dressings. They contain monounsaturated fats that are beneficial for heart health.
- Nuts, seeds, and avocado are excellent sources of healthy fats and can be a valuable addition to snacks or main dishes.
- Pay attention to portion sizes, as even healthy fats are calorie-dense. Moderate consumption of fats can help in preventing weight gain.

Managing Type 2 Diabetes Through Diet

Type 2 diabetes is a condition that requires careful management, including lifestyle and dietary adjustments. Proper nutrition plays a crucial role in controlling blood glucose levels and can significantly improve the quality of life for those living with diabetes.

Basics of a Type 2 Diabetes Diet

1. **Balanced Nutrition**: The foundation of a diabetes diet is balanced nutrition, rich in fiber and low in saturated fats and simple carbohydrates. Your diet should include a large amount of vegetables, whole grains, lean proteins, and healthy fats.
2. **Carbohydrates**: Focus on including complex carbohydrates, especially those rich in fiber. Fiber helps normalize digestive processes and prolongs the feeling of fullness, providing a smoother and more gradual increase in blood sugar after meals.
3. **Glycemic Index**: Preferably choose foods with a low GI, as they cause a slow and gradual rise in blood sugar.
4. **Proteins and Fats**: Choosing lean protein sources, such as poultry, fish, and legumes, as well as healthy fats, including avocado, olive oil, and nuts, helps improve diabetes control and heart health.
5. **Regular Meal Times**: Stable and regular eating helps prevent sharp spikes and drops in blood sugar. Aim to eat at roughly the same times every day.
6. **Reading Labels**: Carefully reading food labels on packaging can help you better understand the carbohydrate, fat, and calorie content of products, facilitating more informed dietary decisions.
7. **Hydration**: Consuming enough fluids is critically important for everyone's health, especially for those with diabetes. Prefer plain water or sugar-free beverages.

8. **Reducing Salt Intake**: Consuming excessive amounts of salt can raise blood pressure, which is particularly dangerous for people with diabetes, as they are already at risk for cardiovascular diseases.

9. **Avoid Processed Foods and Fast Food**: Processed foods often contain hidden sugars and saturated fats. Opt for home-cooked meals made from fresh and natural ingredients.

10. **Watch Portion Sizes**: Using smaller plates can help control portion sizes and prevent overeating.

11. **Consult a Dietitian**: A personal consultation with a dietitian can help you create a meal plan that meets your individual needs and goals for managing diabetes.

Proper nutrition for type 2 diabetes is not about restriction, but an opportunity to enrich your diet with healthy and delicious products that help control blood glucose levels and ensure well-being.

And now, having concluded the formal part, I invite you to an exciting journey into the world of healthy eating, where each recipe is crafted with the thought of supporting you on your path to the best version of yourself, providing not only nourishment for your body but also joy to your eyes and heart, to show you that cuisine for type 2 diabetes can be not only healthy but truly inspiring. Each ingredient in these recipes is chosen deliberately. I aimed to surprise you both with the simplicity of preparation and the sophistication of flavor combinations. From light salads to hearty main dishes, from desserts that don't harm your figure to refreshing drinks — every dish is filled with love and care for your health. A multitude of discoveries awaits you, so grab your apron, and let's dive into the magic of creating wonderful and healthy dishes together!

Ricotta and Raspberry Stuffed Crepes (made with almond flour)

Did You Know? Almond flour, made from ground almonds, is not only a gluten-free alternative to traditional wheat flour but also offers a low-glycemic option for those managing diabetes. It's rich in vitamins, minerals, and healthy fats, making it a fantastic ingredient for creating diabetes-friendly dishes without sacrificing taste or texture.

Yield: 4 servings | **Prep time**: 15 minutes | **Cook time**: 20 minutes

Ingredients:
- 1 cup almond flour
- 3 large eggs
- 1/2 cup almond milk (unsweetened)
- 1 tablespoon erythritol (or another low-glycemic sweetener)
- 1/4 teaspoon salt
- 1 teaspoon vanilla extract
- Cooking spray or butter (for greasing the pan)
- 1 cup ricotta cheese (low-fat)
- 1 cup raspberries (fresh)
- Optional for serving: sugar-free maple syrup, or a few fresh raspberries

Directions:
1. In a mixing bowl, whisk together almond flour, eggs, almond milk, erythritol, salt, and vanilla extract until smooth. Let the batter sit for 5 minutes to thicken slightly.
2. Heat a non-stick skillet over medium heat and lightly grease with cooking spray or butter. Pour about 1/4 cup of batter into the skillet, tilting it to spread the batter evenly into a thin circle.
3. Cook the crepe for 2-3 minutes, or until the edges start to lift from the skillet. Carefully flip with a spatula and cook for another 1-2 minutes on the other side. Transfer to a plate and keep warm. Repeat with the remaining batter.
4. For the filling, gently fold the raspberries into the ricotta cheese, trying not to crush the berries.
5. To assemble, spread a generous amount of the ricotta and raspberry mixture onto half of each crepe. Fold the other half over the filling, then fold once more to create a quarter circle.
6. Serve warm, with a drizzle of sugar-free maple syrup, a sprinkle of powdered erythritol, or fresh raspberries on top, if desired.

Nutritional Information (per serving): 300 calories, 15g protein, 12g carbohydrates, 20g fat, 6g fiber, 180mg cholesterol, 260mg sodium, 200mg potassium.

Whole Grain Avocado Toast with Cherry Tomatoes

Yield: 4 servings | **Prep time**: 10 minutes | **Cook time**: 5 minutes

Ingredients:
- 4 slices of whole grain bread
- 2 ripe avocados
- 1 cup cherry tomatoes, halved
- 1 tablespoon olive oil
- Salt and pepper, to taste
- Optional garnish: fresh basil leaves, balsamic glaze, red pepper flakes

> *Interesting Fact: Avocado is a true record-holder, containing about 20 types of minerals and vitamins. Consuming avocados aids in weight loss, reduces "bad" cholesterol levels in the blood, normalizes blood pressure and cardiovascular system function, helps regulate blood sugar, improves skin and hair condition, enhances vision, and boosts mood.*

Directions:
1. **Toast the Bread:** Lightly toast the whole grain bread slices until they are golden brown and crispy.
2. **Prepare the Avocado Spread:** While the bread is toasting, halve the avocados, remove the pits, and scoop the flesh into a bowl. Mash the avocado with a fork until it reaches your desired consistency. Season with salt and pepper to taste.
3. **Assemble the Toasts:** Spread the mashed avocado evenly over the toasted bread slices. Top each piece of toast with halved cherry tomatoes. Drizzle with olive oil and add any optional garnishes like fresh basil leaves, a drizzle of balsamic glaze, or a sprinkle of red pepper flakes for a spicy kick.
4. **Serve:** Enjoy your avocado toast immediately for the best texture and flavor.

Nutritional Information (per serving): 290 calories, 6g protein, 30g carbohydrates, 17g fat, 9g fiber, 0mg cholesterol, 200mg sodium, 500mg potassium.

Greek Yogurt with Mixed Berries and Nuts

Yield: 4 servings | **Prep time**: 10 minutes | **Cook time**: 0 minutes

Ingredients:
- 2 cups Greek yogurt
- 1 cup mixed berries (strawberries, blueberries, raspberries, blackberries)
- 1/4 cup mixed nuts (almonds, walnuts, pecans), roughly chopped
- 2 tablespoons honey or to taste
- A pinch of ground cinnamon (optional)

Directions:
1. **Prepare the Berries:** Wash the mixed berries and pat them dry. If using strawberries, hull and halve them if they are large.
2. **Assemble the Bowls:** Divide the Greek yogurt equally among four serving bowls.
3. **Add the Berries:** Top each bowl of yogurt with an equal amount of mixed berries.
4. **Add Nuts and Honey:** Sprinkle the chopped nuts over the berries and drizzle with honey. Add a pinch of cinnamon to each bowl if using.
5. **Serve Immediately:** Enjoy the yogurt bowls fresh for the best taste and texture.

Nutritional Information (per serving): 190 calories, 10g protein, 18g carbohydrates, 9g fat, 2g fiber, 5mg cholesterol, 65mg sodium, 200mg potassium.

Sunrise Symphony: Steel-Cut Oats with Cinnamon and Flaxseed

Yield: 4 servings | **Prep time**: 5 minutes | **Cook time**: 30 minutes

Ingredients:
- 1.5 cups steel-cut oats
- 3 cups water
- 1/2 cup milk (any type you prefer, such
- as whole, almond, or soy milk)
- 2 tablespoons ground flaxseed
- 2 teaspoons cinnamon
- 1 tablespoon maple syrup
- 1/2 teaspoon salt
- Fresh berries and nuts, for serving (optional)

Directions:
1. In a medium saucepan, bring 3 cups of water to a boil. Add the steel-cut oats and salt. Reduce the heat to low and simmer uncovered, stirring occasionally, for 20 minutes.
2. Add 1/2 cup of milk and continue to simmer for another 10 minutes, or until the oats are tender and the mixture has thickened to your liking.
3. Stir in the cinnamon, ground flaxseed, and maple syrup. Cook for an additional 2-3 minutes, stirring well.
4. Serve hot, garnished with fresh berries and nuts if desired.

Nutritional Information (per serving): Calories: 215, Protein: 8g, Carbohydrates: 38g, Fat: 4g, Fiber: 6g, Cholesterol: 2mg, Sodium: 150mg, Potassium: 180mg.

Tropical Chia Delight

Yield: 4 servings | **Prep time**: 10 minutes | **Cook time**: 4 hours or overnight

Ingredients:
- 4 cups coconut milk
- 3/4 cup chia seeds
- 2 tablespoons maple syrup, more for serving
- 1 teaspoon vanilla extract
- 2 kiwis, peeled and sliced
- A pinch of salt

Did you know that chia seeds are a superfood rich in antioxidants, minerals, fiber, and omega-3 fatty acids? These tiny seeds pack a powerful punch when it comes to heart health, strengthening the skeletal system, and stabilizing blood sugar levels. Their high antioxidant content helps fight free radicals, reducing inflammation and promoting overall health.

Directions:
1. In a mixing bowl, whisk together the coconut milk, chia seeds, maple syrup, vanilla extract, and a pinch of salt until well combined.
2. Divide the mixture evenly among four serving dishes or glasses.
3. Cover and refrigerate for at least 4 hours, preferably overnight, until the chia seeds have absorbed the liquid and the pudding has thickened.
4. Before serving, stir the pudding once more, top each serving with sliced kiwi, drizzle with additional maple syrup if desired, and sprinkle with shredded coconut

Nutritional Information (per serving): 295 calories, 6g protein, 25g carbohydrates, 19g fat, 10g fiber, 0mg cholesterol, 15mg sodium, 350mg potassium.

Savory Spinach and Mushroom Egg Scramble

Did you know that spinach is not just nutrient-rich, offering a wealth of vitamins A, C, K, iron, calcium, and antioxidants, but also boasts a compelling history of popularity in America? Its fame skyrocketed in the early 20th century, much thanks to the Popeye the Sailor Man cartoon, which showcased the leafy green's strength-enhancing qualities, particularly its iron content. While the immediate effects were exaggerated, the cartoon spotlighted spinach's real health benefits, making it a popular choice in American diets.

Ingredients:

Yield: 4 servings | **Prep time**: 10 minutes | **Cook time**: 10 minutes

- 8 large eggs
- 1 1/2 cups of milk
- 1 cup fresh spinach, chopped
- 1 cup mushrooms, sliced
- 1/2 cup onion, finely chopped
- 1/2 cup shredded cheddar cheese (optional)
- 2 tablespoons olive oil
- Salt and pepper to taste

Directions:
1. In a large bowl, whisk together the eggs, milk, salt, and pepper.
2. Heat olive oil in a large skillet over medium heat. Add the onions and mushrooms, sautéing until the onions are translucent and the mushrooms are golden.
3. Add the chopped spinach to the skillet, cooking until just wilted.
4. Pour the egg mixture into the skillet over the vegetables. Let it sit without stirring for about 1 minute, then gently stir and fold the eggs until they form soft curds and are fully cooked, about 4-6 minutes. Sprinkle cheese over the top in the last minute of cooking if desired.
5. Serve immediately, garnished with additional spinach or fresh herbs if you like.

Nutritional Information *(per serving): 280 calories, 20g protein, 8g carbohydrates, 20g fat, 1g fiber, 390mg cholesterol, 300mg sodium, 400mg potassium.*

Mediterranean Sunrise Muffins

Yield: 6 servings | **Prep time**: 15 minutes | **Cook time**: 20 minutes

Ingredients:
- 8 large eggs
- 1/4 cup almond milk
- 1/2 cup spinach, chopped
- 1/2 cup red bell pepper, diced
- 1/4 cup feta cheese, crumbled
- 1/4 teaspoon salt
- 1/4 teaspoon black pepper
- Cooking spray or olive oil (for greasing the muffin pan)

Directions:
1. Preheat your oven to 375°F (190°C). Grease a 12-cup muffin pan with cooking spray or a light brushing of olive oil.
2. In a large mixing bowl, whisk together the eggs and almond milk until well combined. Season with salt and pepper.
3. Stir in the chopped spinach, diced red bell pepper, and crumbled feta cheese into the egg mixture.
4. Pour the mixture evenly into the prepared muffin cups, filling each about two-thirds full.
5. Bake in the preheated oven for 20 minutes, or until the muffins are set and lightly golden on top.
6. Let the muffins cool for a few minutes before removing them from the pan. Serve warm.

Nutritional Information (per serving): *Approximately 150 calories, 12g protein, 3g carbohydrates, 10g fat, 1g fiber, 200mg cholesterol, 300mg sodium, 200mg potassium.*

Cottage Cheese Delight with Sliced Peaches and Pumpkin Seeds

Yield: 4 servings | **Prep time**: 10 minutes | **Cook time**: 0

Ingredients:
- 2 cups low-fat cottage cheese
- 2 large peaches, ripe but firm, sliced thin
- 1/4 cup pumpkin seeds, toasted
- 1 tablespoon honey (optional, adjust based on dietary needs)
- A pinch of cinnamon for garnishing

Directions:
1. Divide the cottage cheese evenly among four serving bowls.
2. Arrange the sliced peaches beautifully on top of the cottage cheese in each bowl.
3. Sprinkle toasted pumpkin seeds over the peaches and cottage cheese for a delightful crunch.
4. If using, drizzle a small amount of honey over each serving for a touch of sweetness. Remember, the honey is optional and should be used sparingly for those managing diabetes.
5. Garnish each serving with a pinch of cinnamon for added flavor and aroma.
6. Serve immediately, or chill in the refrigerator for an hour before serving for a refreshing and satisfying snack or breakfast.

Nutritional Information (per serving): *150 calories, 14g protein, 15g carbohydrates, 5g fat, 2g fiber, 10mg cholesterol, 300mg sodium, 250mg potassium.*

Savory Mushroom and Zucchini Frittata

Yield: 6 servings | **Prep time**: 15 minutes | **Cook time**: 25 minutes

Ingredients:

- 8 large eggs
- 1/2 cup almond milk (or any milk of your choice)
- 1 tablespoon olive oil
- 1 cup mushrooms, sliced
- 1 medium zucchini, thinly sliced
- 1/2 medium onion, finely chopped
- 1/2 teaspoon salt, or to taste
- 1/4 teaspoon black pepper, or to taste
- 1/4 cup fresh parsley, chopped
- 1/2 cup shredded low-fat cheese (optional)

Did You Know? Mushrooms are not only low in calories and carbohydrates but also rich in selenium, a powerful antioxidant that supports the immune system and prevents cell damage. Additionally, zucchini is a high-fiber vegetable that can help in blood sugar control, making this frittata an excellent choice for those managing type 2 diabetes.

Directions:

1. Preheat your oven to 375°F (190°C).
2. In a large mixing bowl, whisk together the eggs and almond milk until well combined. Season with salt and pepper.
3. Heat olive oil in a 10-inch oven-safe skillet over medium heat. Add the onions, mushrooms, and zucchini. Sauté until the vegetables are soft and slightly golden, about 5-7 minutes.
4. Pour the egg mixture over the sautéed vegetables in the skillet. Gently stir to ensure the vegetables are evenly distributed.
5. Sprinkle the top with fresh parsley and shredded low-fat cheese (if using).
6. Transfer the skillet to the oven and bake for about 18-20 minutes, or until the frittata is set and the top is lightly golden.
7. Let it cool for a few minutes before slicing it into wedges. Serve warm.

Nutritional Information *(per serving): 140 calories, 12g protein, 3g carbohydrates, 9g fat, 1g fiber, 215mg cholesterol, 320mg sodium, 200mg potassium.*

Turkey Bacon and Egg Muffin Cups

Yield: 6 servings | **Prep time**: 10 minutes | **Cook time**: 20 minutes

Ingredients:

- 12 slices of turkey bacon
- 6 large eggs
- 1/4 cup of shredded low-fat cheddar cheese
- Salt and pepper to taste
- Non-stick cooking spray
- Optional: chopped chives or parsley for garnish

Directions:

1. Preheat your oven to 375°F (190°C). Lightly spray a 6-cup muffin tin with non-stick cooking spray.
2. Line each muffin cup with two slices of turkey bacon, arranging them in a circular pattern to create a "cup."
3. Crack an egg into each turkey bacon cup. Season with salt and pepper.
4. Sprinkle the shredded cheddar cheese evenly over each egg.
5. Bake in the preheated oven for about 18-20 minutes, or until the eggs are set and the bacon is crispy.
6. Let the muffin cups cool for a couple of minutes before removing them from the tin. Use a knife or a spatula to gently lift each cup out.
7. Garnish with chopped chives or parsley if desired. Serve warm.

Nutritional Information (per serving): 150 calories, 12g protein, 1g carbohydrates, 10g fat, 0g fiber, 210mg cholesterol, 400mg sodium, 150mg potassium.

> **Interesting Fact:** Turkey bacon is a popular alternative to traditional pork bacon, offering a lower fat content which can be a healthier option for those managing type 2 diabetes. It adds a savory flavor to dishes without the added saturated fats, making these muffin cups a nutritious and satisfying breakfast or snack option.

Vegetable and Hummus Breakfast Burritos

Did You Know? Hummus, a key ingredient in these breakfast burritos, is made from chickpeas, which are known for their ability to help manage blood sugar levels. Chickpeas have a low glycemic index (GI), meaning they cause a slow, steady rise in blood sugar, making them an excellent choice for people with type 2 diabetes. Additionally, the fiber in chickpeas can help improve digestive health and reduce the risk of chronic diseases

Yield: 4 servings | **Prep time**: 15 minutes | **Cook time**: 10 minutes

Ingredients:
- 4 whole grain tortillas
- 1 cup of hummus
- 1 cup of spinach, roughly chopped
- 1 medium bell pepper, diced
- 1 medium zucchini, thinly sliced
- 1/2 cup of red onion, thinly sliced
- 1/2 cup of cherry tomatoes, halved
- 1/4 cup of cilantro, chopped
- 1 tablespoon olive oil
- Salt and pepper to taste

Directions:
1. In a large skillet, heat the olive oil over medium heat. Add the bell pepper, zucchini, and red onion. Cook for 5-7 minutes, or until the vegetables are tender. Season with salt and pepper.
2. Warm the tortillas in a dry skillet or microwave for 10-15 seconds to make them more pliable.
3. Spread a quarter cup of hummus on each tortilla, leaving a small border around the edges.
4. Divide the cooked vegetables evenly among the tortillas. Add the spinach, cherry tomatoes, and cilantro on top of the vegetables.
5. Roll up each tortilla tightly to form a burrito. If desired, you can lightly grill the burritos in a skillet over medium heat for 1-2 minutes on each side to crisp up the tortillas.
6. Serve warm.

Nutritional Information *per serving: 290 calories, 10g protein, 45g carbohydrates, 9g fat, 8g fiber, 0mg cholesterol, 520mg sodium, 370mg potassium.*

Low-Carb Blueberry Muffins

Yield: 6 servings | **Prep time**: 10 min.| **Cook time**: 20 min.

Ingredients:
- 1 1/2 cups almond flour
- 1/4 cup coconut flour
- 1/2 cup erythritol
- 1 teaspoon baking powder
- 1/4 teaspoon salt
- 3 large eggs
- 1/3 cup unsweetened almond milk
- 1/4 cup unsalted butter, melted
- 1 teaspoon vanilla extract
- 1/2 cup fresh or frozen blueberries

> **Interesting Fact**: *Blueberries, known for their high antioxidant content, can help improve insulin response and lower blood sugar levels after meals.*

Directions:
1. Preheat the oven to 350°F (175°C). Line a muffin tin with paper liners or grease it with butter.
2. In a bowl, mix almond flour, coconut flour, erythritol, baking powder, and salt.
3. In another bowl, whisk the eggs, almond milk, melted butter, and vanilla extract until smooth.
4. Combine the wet and dry ingredients, mixing until just combined. Gently fold in the blueberries.
5. Divide the batter evenly among the muffin cups, filling each about 2/3 full.
6. Bake for 20-25 minutes, or until the muffins are golden and a toothpick comes out clean.
7. Let them cool in the pan for 5 minutes before transferring to a wire rack to cool completely.

Nutritional Information *(per serving): Calories 220, Protein 8g, Carbohydrates 12g, Fat 18g, Fiber 4g, Cholesterol 95mg, Sodium 150mg, Potassium 50mg.*

Green Power Protein Smoothie

Directions:

Yield: 2 servings | **Prep time**: 5 minutes | **Cook time**: 0

Ingredients:
- 2 cups fresh spinach
- 1 medium ripe avocado, peeled and pitted
- 1 scoop (about 30g) unsweetened protein powder (whey or plant-based)
- 1 cup unsweetened almond milk (or any milk of your choice)
- 1/2 cup Greek yogurt, plain and unsweetened
- A handful of ice cubes (optional for a colder smoothie)
- Stevia or another low-calorie sweetener, to taste (optional)

1. Place the spinach, avocado, protein powder, almond milk, Greek yogurt, and ice cubes (if using) into a blender.
2. Blend on high until smooth and creamy. Taste and add sweetener if desired, blending again to mix thoroughly.
3. Pour into two glasses and serve immediately for the best taste and texture.

Nutritional Information *(per serving): Approx. 250 calories, 15g protein, 18g carbohydrates, 14g fat, 7g fiber, 5mg cholesterol, 180mg sodium, 600mg potassium.*

Quinoa Berry Delight with Almond Milk

Did You Know? Quinoa is not only a versatile and delicious grain but also a nutritional powerhouse. Quinoa is rich in protein, containing all nine essential amino acids, making it an excellent choice for vegetarians and vegans. It's also high in fiber, minerals, and antioxidants. Plus, it's gluten-free, making it a great option for those with gluten sensitivities or celiac disease

Yield: 4 servings | **Prep time**: 5 minutes | **Cook time**: 20 minutes

Ingredients:
- 1 cup quinoa, rinsed
- 2 cups almond milk, plus more for serving
- 1/2 teaspoon salt
- 2 tablespoons honey or maple syrup
- 1/2 teaspoon vanilla extract
- 1 cup mixed berries (blueberries, strawberries, raspberries)
- 1/4 cup sliced almonds, toasted
- Optional: extra honey or maple syrup for drizzling

Directions:
1. In a medium saucepan, combine the quinoa, almond milk, and salt. Bring to a boil over medium heat.
2. Reduce heat to low, cover, and simmer for 15 to 20 minutes, or until the quinoa is tender and the liquid is mostly absorbed.
3. Remove from heat and stir in the honey (or maple syrup) and vanilla extract.
4. Divide the cooked quinoa among bowls. Top with mixed berries and sliced almonds. Drizzle with additional almond milk and honey or maple syrup if desired.
5. Serve warm or at room temperature for a delightful breakfast or snack.

Nutritional Information (per serving): 235 calories, 8g protein, 40g carbohydrates, 5g fat, 5g fiber, 0mg cholesterol, 150mg sodium, 300mg potassium.

Salads: Fresh and Hearty Combinations

Harbor Fresh: Mixed Greens with Grilled Salmon, Avocado, and Olive Oil Dressing

Did you know that salmon is not only delicious but also incredibly beneficial for health? It's one of the best sources of omega-3 fatty acids, which reduce the risk of heart disease, improve brain function, and can even help combat depression. But here's a fascinating fact: salmon have a unique homing ability. Despite spending most of their lives in the ocean, they return to their native rivers to spawn, navigating thousands of miles and precisely finding their birthplace thanks to their acute sense of smell. This extraordinary phenomenon is still being studied by scientists and remains one of nature's mysteries.

Yield: 4 servings | **Prep time**: 15 minutes | **Cook time**: 10 minutes

Ingredients:
- 4 salmon fillets (4 oz each)
- 8 cups mixed greens (such as spinach, arugula, and romaine lettuce)
- 2 avocados, sliced
- 1/2 red onion, thinly sliced
- 1/4 cup olive oil, plus extra for grilling
- 2 tablespoons lemon juice
- 1 teaspoon Dijon mustard
- Salt and pepper to taste
- Optional: 1 tablespoon chopped fresh dill or parsley for garnish

Directions:
1. Preheat the grill or a grill pan over medium-high heat. Brush the salmon fillets with a little olive oil and season with salt and pepper. Grill the salmon for about 4-5 minutes per side, or until cooked to your liking.
2. In a large bowl, combine the mixed greens and red onion.
3. In a small bowl, whisk together the olive oil, lemon juice, Dijon mustard, salt, and pepper to create the dressing.
4. Divide the salad greens among four plates. Top each with a grilled salmon fillet and sliced avocado.
5. Drizzle the olive oil dressing over each salad and garnish with fresh herbs if using.

Nutritional Information *(per serving): 350 calories, 23g protein, 14g carbohydrates, 25g fat, 7g fiber, 60mg cholesterol, 200mg sodium, 800mg potassium.*

Avocado and Black Bean Salad with Corn, Cilantro, and Tomatoes

Yield: 4 servings | **Prep time**: 15 minutes | **Cook time**: 0 minutes

Ingredients:
- 1 can (15 oz) black beans, rinsed and drained
- 1 large avocado, diced
- 1 cup corn kernels (fresh, canned, or thawed if frozen)
- 1/2 cup cherry tomatoes, halved
- 1/4 cup red onion, finely chopped
- 1/4 cup cilantro, chopped
- Juice of 1 lime
- 2 tablespoons olive oil
- Salt and pepper, to taste

Directions:
1. In a large bowl, combine the black beans, diced avocado, corn kernels, halved cherry tomatoes, and chopped red onion.
2. Add the chopped cilantro to the bowl.
3. In a small bowl, whisk together the lime juice, olive oil, salt, and pepper. Pour this dressing over the salad ingredients.
4. Gently toss everything together until well combined and evenly coated with the dressing.
5. Taste and adjust seasoning with additional salt, pepper, or lime juice if necessary.
6. Serve immediately or chill in the refrigerator for 30 minutes to allow flavors to meld.

Nutritional Information (per serving): 220 calories, 8g protein, 30g carbohydrates, 10g fat, 9g fiber, 300 mg sodium

Arugula Salad with Baked Beets, Goat Cheese, and Walnuts

Yield: 4 servings | **Prep time**: 15 minutes | **Cook time**: 45

Ingredients:
- 4 medium beets, washed and tops trimmed
- 4 cups arugula, washed and dried
- 1/2 cup walnuts, roughly chopped
- 1/4 cup crumbled goat cheese
- 2 tablespoons olive oil (for dressing)
- 1 tablespoon balsamic vinegar
- 1 teaspoon honey (optional, for a touch of sweetness)
- Salt and pepper to taste

Directions:
1. Preheat your oven to 400°F (200°C). Wrap beets in aluminum foil and place them on a baking sheet. Roast in the oven until tender and easily pierced with a fork, about 45 minutes. Once cool enough to handle, peel the beets and cut them into bite-sized pieces.
2. In a large bowl, combine arugula, Baked Beets, walnuts, and goat cheese.
3. In a small bowl, whisk together olive oil, balsamic vinegar, honey (if using), salt, and pepper. Drizzle the dressing over the salad and toss gently to combine.
4. Serve immediately, enjoying the blend of peppery arugula, sweet beets, creamy goat cheese, and crunchy walnuts.

Nutritional Information (per serving): 220 calories, 7g protein, 15g carbohydrates, 16g fat, 4g fiber, 13mg cholesterol, 210mg sodium, 520mg potassium.

Roasted Butternut Squash Salad with Spinach and Pecans

Ingredients:

- 4 cups butternut squash, peeled and cubed
- 2 tablespoons olive oil
- 1/2 teaspoon salt
- 1/4 teaspoon black pepper
- 4 cups fresh spinach leaves
- 1/2 cup pecans, toasted
- 1/4 cup feta cheese, crumbled (optional)
- 2 tablespoons balsamic vinegar
- 1 teaspoon Dijon mustard
- 1 garlic clove, minced
- 1/4 cup extra virgin olive oil

Directions:

1. Preheat the oven to 400°F (200°C). Toss the butternut squash cubes with 2 tablespoons olive oil, salt, and pepper. Spread them on a baking sheet and roast for 25 minutes or until tender and slightly caramelized.
2. In a large salad bowl, combine the roasted butternut squash, fresh spinach, toasted pecans, and crumbled feta cheese.
3. In a small bowl, whisk together the balsamic vinegar, Dijon mustard, minced garlic, and extra virgin olive oil until emulsified. Drizzle the dressing over the salad and gently toss to combine.
4. Serve immediately, or let it sit for about 10 minutes to allow the flavors to meld.

Interesting Fact: Butternut squash is not only delicious but also packed with vitamins A and C, both of which are powerful antioxidants that can help reduce inflammation and boost your immune system.

Nutritional Information (per serving): 290 calories, 4g protein, 18g carbohydrates, 24g fat, 4g fiber, 8mg cholesterol, 320mg sodium, 500mg potassium.

Yield: 4 servings | **Prep time**: 15 minutes | **Cook time**: 25 minutes

Spinach Salad with Grilled Chicken, Strawberries, and Almonds

Yield: 4 servings | **Prep time**: 15 min. | **Cook time**: 10 min.

Ingredients:
- 4 cups fresh spinach leaves, washed and dried
- 1 pound chicken breast, grilled and sliced
- 1 cup strawberries, sliced
- 1/2 cup almonds, toasted and sliced
- 2 tablespoons olive oil
- 1 tablespoon balsamic vinegar
- Salt and pepper, to taste
- Optional: crumbled goat cheese or feta, to taste

Directions:
1. Preheat your grill to medium-high heat. Season the chicken breasts with salt and pepper, and grill for about 5 minutes on each side, or until thoroughly cooked. Let it cool and then slice.
2. In a large bowl, combine the spinach leaves, sliced strawberries, and almonds.
3. In a small bowl, whisk together olive oil and balsamic vinegar with a pinch of salt and pepper to make the dressing.
4. Add the grilled chicken to the salad and toss gently.
5. Drizzle the dressing over the salad and toss again to evenly coat.
6. Serve immediately, garnished with optional cheese if desired.

Nutritional Information *(approximate per serving): 300 calories, 26g protein, 12g carbohydrates, 18g fat, 4g fiber, 55mg cholesterol, 200mg sodium, 500mg potassium.*

Quinoa Tabbouleh with Fresh Herbs and Lemon

Yield: 4 servings | **Prep time:** 15 minutes | **Cook time:** 15 minutes

Ingredients:
- 1 cup quinoa, rinsed
- 2 cups water
- 1/4 cup olive oil
- 1/4 cup fresh lemon juice
- 2 cups fresh parsley, finely chopped
- 1 cup fresh mint leaves, finely chopped
- 2 medium tomatoes, diced
- 1 cucumber, peeled and diced
- 1 small red onion, finely chopped
- Salt and pepper, to taste

Directions:
1. In a medium saucepan, combine quinoa and water. Bring to a boil, then reduce heat to low, cover, and simmer until quinoa is tender and water is absorbed, about 15 minutes. Let it cool to room temperature.
2. In a large bowl, whisk together olive oil and lemon juice. Add the cooled quinoa, parsley, mint, tomatoes, cucumber, and red onion. Toss until well combined. Season with salt and pepper to taste.
3. Refrigerate for at least 1 hour before serving to allow flavors to meld. Serve chilled or at room temperature.

Nutritional Information *(per serving): 300 calories, 8g protein, 40g carbohydrates, 14g fat, 6g fiber, 0mg cholesterol, 20mg sodium, 600mg potassium.*

Broccoli and Cauliflower Salad with Bacon Bits

Ingredients:

- 2 cups broccoli florets, chopped
- 2 cups cauliflower florets, chopped
- 4 slices turkey bacon, cooked and crumbled
- 1/4 cup red onion, finely chopped
- 1/4 cup reduced-fat mayonnaise
- 1/4 cup Greek yogurt
- 1 tablespoon apple cider vinegar
- 1 teaspoon honey (adjust based on dietary needs)
- 1/2 teaspoon salt
- 1/4 teaspoon black pepper
- 2 tablespoons sunflower seeds (optional)
- 2 tablespoons dried cranberries (optional, consider the sugar content)

Directions:

1. Steam the broccoli and cauliflower florets until just tender, about 5-7 minutes. Allow to cool.
2. In a large mixing bowl, combine the cooled broccoli and cauliflower, crumbled turkey bacon, and red onion.
3. In a small bowl, whisk together the mayonnaise, Greek yogurt, apple cider vinegar, honey, salt, and pepper to create the dressing.
4. Pour the dressing over the broccoli, cauliflower, and bacon mixture. Mix thoroughly to ensure even coating
5. If using, sprinkle the sunflower seeds and dried cranberries over the salad just before serving for added texture and sweetness.
6. Serve chilled or at room temperature.

Did you know that broccoli is a powerhouse of essential nutrients and minerals? Rich in vitamins C, K, A, and B, including folic acid, it also offers a healthy dose of fiber for digestive health. Its key antioxidant, sulforaphane, may reduce cancer risk, while potassium supports cardiovascular health by regulating blood pressure. Vitamin K is crucial for blood clotting and bone health. Incorporating broccoli into your diet can bolster immunity, protect cells from free radical damage, and promote skin health through collagen production. Truly, broccoli is a versatile vegetable that enhances both the flavor and nutritional value of any dish.

Nutritional Information (per serving): Approximately 150 calories, 8g protein, 12g carbohydrates, 7g fat, 3g fiber, 20mg cholesterol, 400mg sodium.

Yield: 4 servings | **Prep time**: 15 minutes | **Cook time**: 10 minutes

Caprese Salad with Balsamic Glaze (Sugar-Free)

Yield: 4 servings | **Prep time**: 10 min. | **Cook time**: 0 min.

Ingredients:
- 4 large ripe tomatoes, sliced
- 1 pound fresh mozzarella cheese, sliced
- 1/4 cup fresh basil leaves
- 2 tablespoons extra virgin olive oil
- Salt and pepper, to taste
- 1/4 cup balsamic vinegar (sugar-free)

Directions:
1. Arrange the tomato and mozzarella slices on a platter, alternating them and overlapping slightly.
2. Scatter the basil leaves over the tomatoes and mozzarella.
3. Drizzle the olive oil evenly over the salad, and season with salt and pepper.
4. In a small saucepan, reduce the balsamic vinegar over medium heat until thickened, about 5-7 minutes. Let it cool, then drizzle over the salad just before serving.

Nutritional Information (per serving): 300 calories, 20g protein, 10g carbohydrates, 20g fat, 2g fiber, 50mg cholesterol, 400mg sodium, 300mg potassium.

Mediterranean Chickpea Salad with Olives and Peppers

Yield: 4 servings | **Prep time**: 15 minutes | **Cook time**: 0 min.

Ingredients:

- 2 cans (15 ounces each) chickpeas, drained and rinsed
- 1 cup cherry tomatoes, halved
- 1/2 cup Kalamata olives, pitted and sliced
- 1/2 cup roasted red peppers, sliced
- 1/4 cup red onion, finely chopped
- 1/4 cup fresh parsley, chopped
- 1/4 cup feta cheese, crumbled (optional for a non-dairy version)
- 3 tablespoons extra virgin olive oil
- 2 tablespoons lemon juice
- 1 garlic clove, minced
- 1 teaspoon dried oregano
- Salt and pepper, to taste

Directions:
1. In a large mixing bowl, combine chickpeas, cherry tomatoes, Kalamata olives, roasted red peppers, red onion, and fresh parsley.
2. In a small bowl, whisk together the extra virgin olive oil, lemon juice, minced garlic, dried oregano, salt, and pepper to create the dressing.
3. Pour the dressing over the salad ingredients and toss well to coat evenly.
4. Sprinkle feta cheese over the salad and gently mix.
5. Refrigerate the salad for at least 30 minutes before serving to allow the flavors to meld.

Nutritional Information (per serving): 280 calories, 10g protein, 35g carbohydrates, 12g fat, 9g fiber, 15mg cholesterol, 400mg sodium, 450mg potassium.

Grilled Asparagus and Quail Egg Salad

Ingredients:

- 1 lb asparagus, trimmed
- 15 quail eggs
- 2 tablespoons olive oil
- Salt and pepper, to taste
- 4 cups mixed salad greens
- 1/4 cup shaved Parmesan cheese
- 2 tablespoons balsamic vinegar
- 1 teaspoon Dijon mustard
- 1/4 cup extra virgin olive oil
- Optional: cherry tomatoes, halved, for garnish

Directions:

1. Preheat your grill to medium-high heat. Toss asparagus with 2 tablespoons of olive oil and season with salt and pepper. Grill until tender and slightly charred, about 3-4 minutes per side. Let it cool, then chop into bite-sized pieces.
2. Boil a pot of water and gently add the quail eggs. Cook for 2 minutes for soft-boiled eggs or 4 minutes for hard-boiled. Remove, cool in ice water, and then peel.
3. Whisk together balsamic vinegar, Dijon mustard, and extra virgin olive oil in a small bowl. Season the dressing with salt and pepper to your liking.
4. Toss the mixed greens with the grilled asparagus and prepared dressing in a large bowl.
5. Distribute the salad evenly among plates. Top each serving with quail eggs (around 3-4 eggs per plate), cut in half, and sprinkle with shaved Parmesan cheese. Add cherry tomatoes as a garnish if desired.
6. Serve this delightful salad immediately for the

Did you know asparagus is not only low in calories but also packed with essential vitamins and minerals? It's a great source of vitamins A, C, E, K, and B6, as well as folate, iron, copper, calcium, protein, and fiber. Thanks to its high-water content, asparagus helps with hydration and provides a variety of health benefits, including improved digestion, weight management, and reduced blood pressure. This makes it an invaluable addition to a healthy diet, particularly for those managing diabetes or looking to maintain a balanced lifestyle.

Nutritional Information (per serving): 250 calories, 12g protein, 9g carbohydrates, 19g fat, 3g fiber, 290mg cholesterol, 340mg sodium, 400mg potassium

Yield: 4 servings | **Prep time**: 15 minutes | **Cook time**: 10 minutes

Asian Slaw with Cabbage, Carrots, and Sesame Ginger Dressing

Yield: 4 servings | **Prep time**: 15 min. | **Cook time**: 0 min.

Ingredients:

- 4 cups shredded cabbage (mix of purple and green for color)
- 1 cup shredded carrots
- 1/4 cup thinly sliced green onions
- 1/4 cup chopped fresh cilantro
- 2 tablespoons sesame seeds, toasted

For the Sesame Ginger Dressing:

- 3 tablespoons rice vinegar
- 2 tablespoons sesame oil
- 1 tablespoon soy sauce (low sodium)
- 1 tablespoon grated fresh ginger
- 1 clove garlic, minced
- 1 teaspoon sugar substitute (stevia or monk fruit)
- Salt and pepper to taste

Directions:

1. In a large bowl, combine the shredded cabbage, carrots, green onions, and cilantro.
2. In a small bowl, whisk together the rice vinegar, sesame oil, low sodium soy sauce, grated ginger, minced garlic, and sugar substitute until well combined. Season with salt and pepper to taste.
3. Pour the dressing over the cabbage mixture and toss until everything is well coated. Let the slaw sit for about 10 minutes to allow the flavors to meld together.
4. Just before serving, sprinkle with toasted sesame seeds for added crunch and flavor.

Nutritional Information *(per serving): 100 calories, 2g protein, 10g carbohydrates, 7g fat, 3g fiber, 0mg cholesterol, 150mg sodium, 200mg potassium.*

Apple, Walnut, and Celery Salad with Greek Yogurt Dressing

Yield: 4 servings | **Prep time**: 15 minutes | **Cook time**: 0 min.

Ingredients:

- 2 large apples, cored and thinly sliced
- 1 cup walnuts, roughly chopped
- 4 stalks celery, thinly sliced
- 1/2 cup Greek yogurt
- 2 tablespoons lemon juice
- 1 tablespoon honey (or substitute with a suitable sweetener for diabetics)
- 1 teaspoon Dijon mustard
- Salt and pepper, to taste
- Mixed salad greens, for serving

Directions:

1. In a large mixing bowl, combine the sliced apples, chopped walnuts, and sliced celery.
2. In a small bowl, whisk together Greek yogurt, lemon juice, honey, and Dijon mustard until smooth. Season with salt and pepper to taste.
3. Pour the dressing over the apple mixture and toss gently to coat everything evenly.
4. Serve the salad over a bed of mixed salad greens for added texture and color.

Nutritional Information *(per serving): 250 calories, 6g protein, 24g carbohydrates, 16g fat, 4g fiber, 5mg cholesterol, 120mg sodium, 300mg potassium.*

Shrimp and Avocado Salad with Citrus Dressing

Ingredients:

- 1 lb (about 450g) shrimp, peeled and deveined
- 2 ripe avocados, diced
- 4 cups mixed greens (e.g., arugula, spinach, romaine)
- 1 small red onion, thinly sliced
- 1/2 cup cherry tomatoes, halved
- 1/4 cup fresh cilantro, chopped
- 2 tablespoons olive oil
- Salt and pepper, to taste

For the Citrus Dressing:
- 1/4 cup fresh orange juice
- 1/4 cup fresh lime juice
- 1 tablespoon olive oil
- 1 teaspoon honey (or a suitable sugar-free sweetener)
- 1 garlic clove, minced
- Salt and pepper, to taste

Directions:

1. In a large skillet over medium heat, heat the olive oil and cook the shrimp for about 2-3 minutes on each side or until they are pink and cooked through. Season with salt and pepper. Remove from heat and let cool.
2. In a large mixing bowl, combine the mixed greens, red onion, cherry tomatoes, and cilantro.
3. Add the cooled shrimp and diced avocados to the salad mix.
4. To make the dressing, whisk together the orange juice, lime juice, olive oil, honey (or sweetener), minced garlic, and salt and pepper in a small bowl until well combined.
5. Drizzle the citrus dressing over the salad and gently toss to ensure everything is evenly coated.
6. Serve immediately, garnished with extra cilantro if desired.

Did you know that shrimp, a popular seafood choice around the globe, can be a fantastic addition to a diabetic-friendly diet? Despite their small size, shrimp pack a substantial nutritional punch. They are an excellent source of high-quality protein and provide important nutrients, including selenium, vitamin B12, and phosphorus. What's particularly interesting for those managing Type 2 diabetes is that shrimp have a very low glycemic index, meaning they won't spike blood sugar levels. Plus, they contain astaxanthin, an antioxidant that may help reduce inflammation and improve insulin sensitivity. Incorporating shrimp into your meals not only brings a taste of the ocean to your table but also supports a balanced, healthful diet.

Nutritional Information (per serving): 320 calories, 24g protein, 18g carbohydrates, 18g fat, 7g fiber, 180mg cholesterol, 300mg sodium, 650mg potassium

Yield: 4 servings | **Prep time**: 20 minutes | **Cook time**: 10 minutes

Chicken and Vegetable Soup with Herbs

Ingredients:

- 1 tablespoon olive oil
- 1 lb chicken breast, diced
- 1 medium onion, chopped
- 2 carrots, peeled and diced
- 2 stalks celery, diced
- 3 cloves garlic, minced
- 4 cups low-sodium chicken broth
- 1 cup water
- 1 teaspoon dried thyme
- 1 teaspoon dried rosemary
- 1 bay leaf
- 1 cup chopped zucchini
- 1 cup green beans, trimmed and cut into 1-inch pieces
- Salt and pepper to taste
- Fresh parsley, chopped, for garnish

Directions:

1. Heat the olive oil in a large pot over medium heat. Add the chicken and cook until browned on all sides, about 5-7 minutes. Remove the chicken from the pot and set aside.
2. In the same pot, add the onion, carrots, and celery. Cook until the vegetables begin to soften, about 5 minutes. Add the garlic and cook for another minute.
3. Return the chicken to the pot. Add the chicken broth, water, thyme, rosemary, and bay leaf. Bring to a simmer, then reduce the heat to low and cover. Simmer for about 20 minutes.
4. Add the zucchini and green beans to the pot. Continue to simmer until the vegetables are tender, about 10 minutes more. Remove the bay leaf.
5. Season the soup with salt and pepper to taste. Serve hot, garnished with fresh parsley.

Nutritional Information (per serving): 250 calories, 27g protein, 18g carbohydrates, 7g fat, 4g fiber, 55mg cholesterol, 200mg sodium, 400mg potassium.

Yield: 4 servings | **Prep time**: 15 minutes | **Cook time**: 30 minutes

Vegetable Lentil Soup with Kale

Ingredients:

- 1 cup dried lentils, rinsed
- 2 tablespoons olive oil
- 1 onion, diced
- 2 carrots, peeled and diced
- 2 stalks celery, diced
- 2 cloves garlic, minced
- 1 teaspoon ground cumin
- 1/2 teaspoon ground coriander
- 1/4 teaspoon smoked paprika
- 1 bay leaf
- 6 cups vegetable broth
- 1 can (14 oz) diced tomatoes, undrained
- 2 cups chopped kale, stems removed
- Salt and pepper, to taste
- Juice of 1 lemon
- Fresh parsley, chopped (for garnish)

Directions:

1. In a large pot, heat the olive oil over medium heat. Add the onion, carrots, and celery, and sauté until they begin to soften, about 5 minutes.
2. Add the garlic, cumin, coriander, smoked paprika, and bay leaf, and cook for another minute, stirring to combine the flavors.
3. Add the lentils, vegetable broth, and diced tomatoes with their juice. Bring the mixture to a boil, then reduce heat, cover, and simmer for about 30 minutes, or until the lentils are tender.
4. Stir in the chopped kale and continue to simmer for another 10-15 minutes, until the kale is tender.
5. Remove from heat, discard the bay leaf, and stir in the lemon juice. Season with salt and pepper to taste.
6. Serve hot, garnished with fresh parsley.

Did you know that Lentils are not only an excellent source of plant-based protein but also rich in dietary iron, which is crucial for transporting oxygen in the blood and supporting energy levels? Kale, on the other hand, is loaded with vitamins A, C, and K, making this soup an immune-boosting meal that also helps with blood clotting and bone health. Additionally, the high fiber content in both lentils and kale promotes digestive health and can help stabilize blood sugar levels, making this soup an especially smart choice for a hearty, healthful meal.

Nutritional Information *(per serving):* *Calories: 250, Protein: 12g, Carbohydrates: 38g, Fat: 6g, Fiber: 15g, Cholesterol: 0mg, Sodium: 300mg, Potassium: 700mg.*

Yield: 6 servings | **Prep time**: 15 minutes | **Cook time**: 45 minutes

Spicy Tomato and Bell Pepper Soup

Ingredients:

- 1 tablespoon olive oil
- 2 cloves garlic, minced
- 1 medium onion, diced
- 2 bell peppers (1 red, 1 yellow), diced
- 2 cans (14.5 ounces each) diced tomatoes, no salt added
- 1 teaspoon smoked paprika
- 1/2 teaspoon red pepper flakes (adjust according to taste)
- 1 quart low-sodium vegetable broth
- Salt and pepper to taste
- Fresh basil for garnish (optional)
- 1 tablespoon balsamic vinegar (optional, for a slight sweetness and depth)

Directions:

1. In a large pot, heat the olive oil over medium heat. Add the garlic and onion, sautéing until softened, about 3-5 minutes. Add the bell peppers and cook for an additional 5 minutes or until just tender.
2. Stir in the diced tomatoes, smoked paprika, and red pepper flakes. Cook for a few minutes to let the flavors meld.
3. Pour in the vegetable broth and bring the mixture to a boil. Reduce heat and simmer for about 20 minutes, allowing the flavors to combine.
4. For a smoother soup, carefully transfer the soup to a blender and blend until smooth, or use an immersion blender directly in the pot.
5. Taste and adjust the seasoning with salt and pepper. If using, stir in the balsamic vinegar.
6. Ladle the soup into bowls, garnishing with fresh basil if desired. Serve hot.

Nutritional Information (per serving): 150 calories, 3g protein, 20g carbohydrates, 5g fat, 5g fiber, 300mg sodium, 600mg potassium.

Did you know that tomatoes are a fantastic source of lycopene, an antioxidant that has been linked to reduced risk of heart disease and cancer? Meanwhile, bell peppers are loaded with vitamin C, which not only supports the immune system but also enhances the absorption of iron from your diet, promoting healthy blood flow. Furthermore, the capsaicin found in the spicy components of the soup, like chili peppers, may boost metabolism and aid in fat loss. This soup is not just a feast for your senses; it's also a powerful ally for your health.

Yield: 4 servings | **Prep time**: 15 minutes | **Cook time**: 30 minutes

Butternut Squash and Carrot Soup

Ingredients:

- 1 medium butternut squash, peeled, seeded, and cubed
- 4 large carrots, peeled and sliced
- 1 medium onion, diced
- 3 cloves of garlic, minced
- 4 cups of vegetable broth
- 1 teaspoon of ground cinnamon
- 1/2 teaspoon of ground nutmeg
- Salt and pepper to taste
- 2 tablespoons of olive oil
- Fresh parsley, chopped, for garnish
- Optional: a dollop of Greek yogurt or coconut milk for serving

Directions:

1. Heat the olive oil in a large pot over medium heat. Add the onion and garlic, and sauté until they are soft and translucent, about 5 minutes.
2. Add the butternut squash and carrots to the pot. Cook for about 10 minutes, stirring occasionally, until the vegetables start to soften.
3. Pour the vegetable broth into the pot. Add cinnamon, nutmeg, salt, and pepper. Bring to a boil, then reduce the heat and simmer, covered, for about 20 minutes or until the squash and carrots are tender.
4. Use an immersion blender to puree the soup directly in the pot until smooth. Alternatively, you can transfer the soup in batches to a blender and puree until smooth.
5. Serve hot, garnished with fresh parsley. For a creamier soup, add a dollop of Greek yogurt or a swirl of coconut milk before serving.

Nutritional Information *(per serving): 180 calories, 3g protein, 30g carbohydrates, 5g fat, 6g fiber, 0mg cholesterol, 710mg sodium, 790mg potassium.*

Did you know *that butternut squash and carrots both contain high levels of beta-carotene, which the body converts into vitamin A? This essential nutrient is crucial for maintaining healthy vision, skin health, and immune function. Furthermore, butternut squash is a great source of fiber, which can help to promote a healthy digestive system and keep you feeling full longer. This makes the Butternut Squash and Carrot Soup not only a treat for your taste buds but also a nourishing choice for your overall health.*

Yield: 4 servings | **Prep time**: 20 minutes | **Cook time**: 35 minutes

Miso Soup with Tofu and Seaweed

Yield: 4 servings | **Prep time**: 10 min. | **Cook time**: 15 min.

Ingredients:
- 4 cups water
- 2 tablespoons miso paste (preferably low-sodium for a healthier option)
- 1 cup firm tofu, cubed
- 1/2 cup seaweed (wakame or nori), rehydrated and chopped
- 2 green onions, thinly sliced
- 1 tablespoon soy sauce (low sodium)
- 1 teaspoon sesame oil

Directions:
1. In a medium pot, bring the water to a simmer over medium heat.
2. In a small bowl, mix the miso paste with a little hot water to dissolve. Add this mixture back into the pot of simmering water.
3. Add the cubed tofu and rehydrated seaweed to the pot. Allow the soup to simmer gently for about 10 minutes, ensuring it doesn't boil to preserve the miso's beneficial properties.
4. Stir in the soy sauce and sesame oil, and simmer for an additional 5 minutes.
5. Serve the soup in bowls, garnished with sliced green onions.

Nutritional Information *(approximate per serving): 90 calories, 6g protein, 7g carbohydrates, 4g fat, 2g fiber, 0mg cholesterol, 27400mg sodium, 150mg potassium.*

Gazpacho

Yield: 4 servings | **Prep time**: 20 minutes | **Cook time**: 0 minutes

Ingredients:
- 1 1/2 pounds ripe tomatoes, peeled and chopped
- 1 cucumber, peeled, seeded, and chopped
- 1 bell pepper (red or green), seeded and chopped
- 1 small red onion, chopped
- 2 cloves garlic, minced
- 2 tablespoons olive oil
- 2 tablespoons red wine vinegar
- Salt and pepper to taste
- 2 cups tomato juice
- Optional garnishes: diced cucumber, bell pepper, croutons, chopped hard-boiled eggs, or fresh herbs

Directions:
1. Combine tomatoes, cucumber, bell pepper, onion, garlic, olive oil, and red wine vinegar in a large bowl. Season with salt and pepper.
2. Transfer half of the mixture to a blender and puree until smooth. Return the pureed mixture to the bowl.
3. Stir in the tomato juice and adjust seasonings as necessary. Cover and chill in the refrigerator for at least 2 hours, preferably overnight.
4. Serve cold, garnished with your choice of diced cucumber, bell pepper, croutons, chopped hard-boiled eggs, or fresh herbs.

Nutritional Information *(per serving): 150 calories, 3g protein, 18g carbohydrates, 8g fat, 4g fiber, 0mg cholesterol*

Split Pea Soup with Ham

Ingredients:

- 1 lb dried split peas
- 8 cups low-sodium chicken broth
- 1 lb ham, cubed
- 2 carrots, diced
- 2 stalks celery, diced
- 1 large onion, chopped
- 2 cloves garlic, minced
- 1 bay leaf
- 1/2 teaspoon dried thyme
- Salt and pepper to taste

Directions:

1. In a large pot, combine split peas and chicken broth. Bring to a boil, then reduce heat to simmer, skimming off any foam.
2. Add ham, carrots, celery, onion, garlic, bay leaf, and thyme. Season with salt and pepper.
3. Cover and simmer for about 1.5 hours, or until peas are tender and the soup has thickened, stirring occasionally.
4. Remove the bay leaf before serving. Adjust seasoning as needed.

Nutritional Information (per serving): Calories: 350, Protein: 25g, Carbohydrates: 45g, Fat: 8g, Fiber: 16g, Cholesterol: 30mg, Sodium: 700mg, Potassium: 850mg

Did you know that peas are not only one of the oldest cultivated vegetables known to humans but also a powerhouse of nutrition? Nutritionally, peas are packed with plant-based protein, fiber, and essential vitamins and minerals, including vitamin C, vitamin K, and several B vitamins. They're also rich in antioxidants and have a low glycemic index, which makes them an excellent choice for maintaining stable blood sugar levels. This combination of benefits makes peas an incredibly versatile and beneficial addition to any diet, underscoring their longstanding value to human health and cuisine.

Yield: 4 servings | **Prep time**: 10 minutes | **Cook time:** 1 hour 30 minutes

Mushroom and Barley Soup

Ingredients:

- 1 cup pearl barley
- 4 cups low-sodium vegetable broth
- 2 cups water
- 1 lb fresh mushrooms, sliced (a mix of button and cremini works well)
- 1 large onion, diced
- 2 carrots, peeled and diced
- 2 celery stalks, diced
- 2 cloves garlic, minced
- 1 tablespoon olive oil
- 1 teaspoon dried thyme
- Salt and pepper to taste
- Fresh parsley, chopped for garnish

Directions:

1. Rinse the barley under cold water until the water runs clear. Set aside.
2. In a large pot, heat the olive oil over medium heat. Add the onions, carrots, and celery, and cook until they start to soften, about 5 minutes.
3. Add the garlic and mushrooms, and cook for another 5 minutes, until the mushrooms have reduced in size and released their moisture.
4. Add the barley, vegetable broth, water, thyme, salt, and pepper. Bring to a boil, then reduce the heat to low and simmer, covered, for about 35-40 minutes, or until the barley is tender.
5. Taste and adjust seasoning as necessary. Serve hot, garnished with fresh parsley.

Nutritional Information (approximate per serving): 250 calories, 8g protein, 45g carbohydrates, 4g fat, 10g fiber, 0mg cholesterol, 300mg sodium, 600mg potassium.

Did you know that Mushroom and Barley Soup not only warms you up on a cold day but also serves as a nutritional powerhouse? Barley, a key ingredient, is loaded with beta-glucan, a type of fiber that's been shown to lower cholesterol and stabilize blood sugar levels. Meanwhile, mushrooms are not just for flavor; they're rich in B vitamins, selenium, and powerful antioxidants. These components are known to boost the immune system and reduce inflammation. Together, mushrooms and barley offer a symbiotic blend that supports heart health and boosts immunity, all while delivering a deliciously earthy and satisfying meal.

Yield: 4 servings | **Prep time**: 15 minutes | **Cook time**: 45 minutes

Turkey and White Bean Chili

Ingredients:

- 1 lb ground turkey
- 1 tablespoon olive oil
- 1 large onion, diced
- 2 cloves garlic, minced
- 2 cans (15 oz each) white beans, drained and rinsed
- 1 can (14.5 oz) diced tomatoes
- 4 cups chicken broth
- 1 teaspoon ground cumin
- 1 teaspoon chili powder
- 1/2 teaspoon paprika
- Salt and pepper to taste
- Optional toppings: chopped cilantro, shredded cheese, sliced jalapeños

Directions:

1. In a large pot, heat the olive oil over medium heat. Add the turkey and cook until browned, breaking it apart with a spoon, about 5-7 minutes.
2. Add the onion and garlic to the pot and sauté until the onion is translucent, about 5 minutes.
3. Stir in the white beans, diced tomatoes, chicken broth, cumin, chili powder, paprika, salt, and pepper. Bring to a simmer.
4. Reduce the heat to low and let the chili simmer, uncovered, for 30 minutes, stirring occasionally.
5. Serve hot, with optional toppings if desired.

Nutritional Information (per serving): 320 calories, 22g protein, 34g carbohydrates, 9g fat, 8g fiber, 55mg cholesterol, 890mg sodium, 700mg potassium.

Did you know that Turkey, being a lean source of protein, provides all the essential amino acids your body needs without the extra fat found in red meats? White beans, on the other hand, are an excellent source of fiber, which can help lower cholesterol and stabilize blood sugar levels. Additionally, they are rich in iron and protein, making this dish a hearty, nutritious option. The combination of turkey and white beans in this chili not only makes for a deliciously hearty meal but also supports muscle growth and energy production, making it a perfect dish for health-conscious food lovers.

Yield: 6 servings | **Prep time**: 15 minutes | **Cook time**: 45 minutes

Pork Tenderloin with Apple Cider Vinegar Glaze

Yield: 4 servings | **Prep time**: 10 minutes | **Cook time**: 25 minutes

Ingredients:
- 1 (1.5-pound) pork tenderloin
- Salt and pepper, to taste
- 2 tablespoons olive oil
- 1/4 cup apple cider vinegar
- 1 tablespoon honey
- 1 teaspoon Dijon mustard
- 1 garlic clove, minced
- 1/2 teaspoon dried thyme
- 1/4 cup chicken broth

Directions:
1. Preheat your oven to 375°F (190°C). Season the pork tenderloin with salt and pepper.
2. In a large ovenproof skillet, heat olive oil over medium-high heat. Add the pork and sear until all sides are golden brown about 5 minutes.
3. In a bowl, whisk together apple cider vinegar, honey, Dijon mustard, garlic, and thyme. Pour this mixture over the pork in the skillet.
4. Place the skillet in the preheated oven and roast the pork for 15-20 minutes, or until a thermometer inserted into the thickest part reads 145°F (63°C).
5. Remove from oven, transfer the pork to a cutting board, and let it rest for 5 minutes. Meanwhile, place the skillet over medium heat, add chicken broth, and simmer the sauce until it thickens slightly, about 5 minutes. Slice the pork and serve with the glaze.

Nutritional Information *(per serving): 310 calories, 35g protein, 10g carbohydrates, 12g fat, 0g fiber, 90mg cholesterol, 290mg sodium, 360mg potassium.*

Grilled Lamb Chops with Mint Pesto

Yield: 4 servings | **Prep time**: 15 min. | **Cook time**: 10 min.

Ingredients:
- 8 lamb chops
- 2 tablespoons olive oil
- Salt and freshly ground black pepper, to taste

For the Mint Pesto:
- 1 cup fresh mint leaves
- 1/2 cup fresh parsley leaves
- 1/4 cup grated Parmesan cheese
- 1/4 cup pine nuts or walnuts
- 2 cloves garlic, minced
- 1/2 cup olive oil
- Salt and freshly ground black pepper, to taste

Directions:
1. Preheat the grill to medium-high heat. Rub the lamb chops with olive oil and season with salt and pepper.
2. Grill the lamb chops for 4-5 minutes on each side for medium-rare, or until they reach the desired doneness.
3. For the mint pesto, combine mint leaves, parsley, Parmesan cheese, nuts, and garlic in a food processor. Pulse until coarsely chopped. With the processor running, gradually add olive oil until the mixture is smooth. Season with salt and pepper.
4. Serve the grilled lamb chops with a generous spoonful of mint pesto on top.

Nutritional Information (per serving): 400 calories, 30g protein, 5g carbohydrates, 30g fat, 3g fiber, 87.5mg cholesterol, 250mg sodium, 350mg potassium

Beef and Vegetable Kebabs with Yogurt Tahini Sauce

Yield: 4 servings | **Prep time**: 20 min. | **Cook time**: 10 min.

Ingredients:
- 1 pound lean beef (like sirloin), cut into 1-inch cubes
- 2 bell peppers (any color), cut into 1-inch pieces
- 1 large red onion, cut into wedges
- 1 zucchini, cut into 1/2-inch slices
- 1/2 cup plain Greek yogurt
- 2 tablespoons tahini
- 1 lemon, juiced
- 2 cloves garlic, minced
- 1 teaspoon ground cumin
- Salt and pepper, to taste
- Optional garnishes: fresh parsley, lemon wedges

Directions:
1. Preheat your grill to medium-high heat. Thread beef, bell peppers, onion, and zucchini alternately onto skewers.
2. In a small bowl, mix Greek yogurt, tahini, lemon juice, garlic, and cumin. Season with salt and pepper to taste. Set aside some sauce for serving and brush a little over the kebabs before grilling.
3. Grill kebabs, turning occasionally, until beef is cooked to desired doneness and vegetables are tender, about 8-10 minutes.
4. Serve kebabs with a side of the yogurt tahini sauce and garnish with fresh parsley and lemon wedges if desired.

Nutritional Information (per serving): 350 calories, 26g protein, 18g carbohydrates, 20g fat, 3g fiber, 75mg cholesterol, 200mg sodium, 650mg potassium

Slow Cooker Pulled Pork with Sugar-Free BBQ Sauce

Ingredients:

- 2 pounds pork shoulder
- Salt and pepper, to taste
- 1 onion, thinly sliced
- 3 cloves garlic, minced
- 1 cup sugar-free BBQ sauce
- 1/4 cup apple cider vinegar
- 1 tablespoon smoked paprika
- 1 teaspoon ground cumin
- 1/2 cup chicken or vegetable broth

Directions:

1. Season the pork shoulder with salt and pepper and place it in the slow cooker.
2. Add the sliced onion and minced garlic over the pork.
3. In a bowl, mix the sugar-free BBQ sauce, apple cider vinegar, smoked paprika, and ground cumin. Pour this mixture over the pork.
4. Add the broth to the slow cooker, cover, and cook on low for about 8 hours or until the pork is tender and shreds easily with a fork.
5. Remove the pork from the slow cooker and shred it using two forks. Return the shredded pork to the slow cooker and stir well to coat with the sauce.
6. Serve the pulled pork warm, optionally with a side of coleslaw or on a low-carb bun for a complete meal.

Nutritional Information *(per serving):* 300 calories, 25g protein, 10g carbohydrates, 15g fat, 2g fiber, 90mg cholesterol, 500mg sodium, 400mg potassium.

Yield: 6 servings | **Prep time**: 20 minutes | **Cook time**: 8 hours

Meatballs in a Tomato and Herb Sauce with Zucchini Noodles

Ingredients:

For the Meatballs:
- 1 pound ground beef
- 1/4 cup breadcrumbs
- 1 large egg
- 2 cloves garlic, minced
- 1/2 teaspoon salt
- 1/4 teaspoon black pepper
- 1 teaspoon Italian seasoning

For the Sauce:
- 2 cups tomato sauce
- 1 teaspoon dried basil
- 1 teaspoon dried oregano
- Salt and pepper to taste

For the Zucchini Noodles:
- 4 medium zucchini, spiralized

Yield: 4 servings | **Prep time**: 20 minutes | **Cook time**: 30 minutes

Directions:

1. In a large bowl, mix together the ground meat, breadcrumbs, egg, garlic, salt, pepper, and Italian seasoning. Form into 1-inch balls.
2. In a large skillet over medium heat, cook meatballs until browned and cooked through, about 10 minutes. Remove and set aside.
3. In the same skillet, add the tomato sauce, basil, oregano, salt, and pepper. Bring to a simmer and return the meatballs to the skillet. Cook for an additional 10 minutes.
4. Meanwhile, prepare the zucchini noodles by sautéing them in a separate skillet with a bit of oil for about 3-5 minutes, until tender but still crisp.
5. Serve the meatballs and sauce over the zucchini noodles.

Nutritional Information (per serving): 350 calories, 25g protein, 25g carbohydrates, 15g fat, 5g fiber, 80mg cholesterol, 700mg sodium, 700mg potassium.

Beef Stir-Fry with Broccoli and Bell Peppers

Ingredients:

- 1 lb lean beef (sirloin or flank steak), thinly sliced
- 2 cups broccoli florets
- 1 red bell pepper, thinly sliced
- 1 yellow bell pepper, thinly sliced
- 2 tablespoons soy sauce (low sodium)
- 1 tablespoon olive oil
- 2 cloves garlic, minced
- 1 tablespoon ginger, minced
- 1 tablespoon cornstarch
- 1/4 cup water
- Salt and pepper, to taste

Yield: 4 servings | **Prep time**: 15 minutes | **Cook time**: 10 minutes

Directions:

1. In a small bowl, mix the soy sauce, cornstarch, and water to create a slurry. Set aside.
2. Heat the olive oil in a large skillet or wok over medium-high heat. Add garlic and ginger, sautéing until fragrant, about 1 minute.
3. Add the beef slices to the skillet, seasoning with salt and pepper. Stir-fry until the beef is browned but not fully cooked, about 2-3 minutes.
4. Add the broccoli and bell peppers to the skillet. Continue to stir-fry for an additional 4-5 minutes, or until the vegetables are tender but still crisp.
5. Pour the soy sauce mixture over the beef and vegetables. Stir well to coat everything in the sauce and cook until the sauce has thickened, about 2 minutes.
6. Serve hot, optionally garnished with sesame seeds or green onions.

Nutritional Information (per serving): 250 calories, 26g protein, 15g carbohydrates, 10g fat, 3g fiber, 60mg cholesterol, 350mg sodium, 600mg potassium.

Spiced Rubbed Pork Chops with Grilled Peaches

Ingredients:

- 4 pork chops (about 1-inch thick)
- 2 peaches, halved and pitted
- 2 tablespoons olive oil

For the spice rub:
- 1 teaspoon paprika
- 1 teaspoon garlic powder
- 1 teaspoon onion powder
- 1/2 teaspoon salt
- 1/4 teaspoon black pepper
- 1/4 teaspoon cayenne pepper (optional)

Yield: 4 servings | **Prep time**: 15 minutes | **Cook time**: 20 minutes

Directions:

1. In a small bowl, mix together the ingredients for the spice rub. Apply the rub evenly on both sides of the pork chops.
2. Preheat the grill to medium-high heat. Brush the peach halves and pork chops with olive oil.
3. Place the pork chops on the grill. Cook for about 7-10 minutes per side, or until the internal temperature reaches 145°F (63°C).
4. During the last few minutes of cooking the pork chops, place the peach halves on the grill, cut-side down. Grill until they are soft and have grill marks, about 4-5 minutes.
5. Serve the pork chops with the grilled peaches on the side.

Nutritional Information *(per serving): 300 calories, 25g protein, 15g carbohydrates, 15g fat, 2g fiber, 75mg cholesterol, 350mg sodium, 500mg potassium*

Stuffed Peppers with Ground Beef and Cauliflower Rice

Ingredients:

- 4 large bell peppers, halved and seeds removed
- 1 pound lean ground beef
- 2 cups cauliflower rice
- 1 medium onion, finely chopped
- 2 cloves garlic, minced
- 1 cup low-sodium diced tomatoes, drained
- 1 teaspoon ground cumin
- 1 teaspoon smoked paprika
- Salt and pepper, to taste
- 1/2 cup low-fat shredded cheese (optional, for topping)
- Fresh parsley, for garnishing

Yield: 4 servings | **Prep time**: 20 minutes | **Cook time**: 45 minutes

Directions:

1. Preheat oven to 375°F (190°C). Arrange bell pepper halves in a baking dish.
2. In a skillet over medium heat, cook the ground beef, onion, and garlic until beef is browned. Drain excess fat.
3. Stir in cauliflower rice, diced tomatoes, cumin, paprika, salt, and pepper. Cook for 5 minutes, or until mixture is heated through.
4. Spoon the beef and cauliflower rice mixture into each bell pepper half. Top with shredded cheese if using.
5. Bake in the preheated oven for 25-30 minutes, or until peppers are tender.
6. Garnish with fresh parsley before serving.

Nutritional Information (per serving): 350 kcal calories, 26g protein, 18g carbohydrates, 18g fat, 5g fiber, 70mg cholesterol, 300mg sodium, 800mg potassium.

Beef and Broccoli Stir-Fry

Ingredients:

- 1 lb lean beef (sirloin or flank steak), thinly sliced against the grain
- 4 cups broccoli florets
- 2 tablespoons vegetable oil
- 1 tablespoon minced garlic
- 1 tablespoon minced ginger
- 1/4 cup low-sodium soy sauce
- 1 tablespoon oyster sauce (optional)
- 1 teaspoon cornstarch dissolved in 2 tablespoons water
- Salt and pepper to taste
- Cooked rice or noodles, for serving

Yield: 4 servings | **Prep time**: 15 minutes | **Cook time**: 10 minutes

Directions:

1. Heat 1 tablespoon of the oil in a large skillet or wok over high heat. Add the beef in a single layer, letting it sear without stirring for about 1 minute. Stir-fry until just cooked through, then remove from the skillet and set aside.
2. In the same skillet, add the remaining tablespoon of oil, garlic, and ginger. Sauté for about 30 seconds, then add the broccoli. Stir-fry for about 2 minutes, adding a splash of water if needed to help steam the broccoli.
3. Return the beef to the skillet. Add the soy sauce and oyster sauce if using. Stir the cornstarch slurry again before adding it to the skillet. Cook, stirring, until the sauce has thickened and the beef and broccoli are well-coated, about 2 minutes.
4. Season with salt and pepper to taste. Serve hot over rice or noodles.

Nutritional Information (per serving): 300 calories, 25g protein, 15g carbohydrates, 15g fat, 3g fiber, 70mg cholesterol, 600mg sodium, 700mg potassium.

Low-Carb Meatloaf with Ground Turkey and Bell Peppers

Ingredients:

- 1 pound ground turkey
- 1/2 cup finely chopped bell peppers (mix of colors)
- 1/4 cup almond flour
- 1 large egg
- 2 tablespoons tomato paste
- 1 teaspoon garlic powder
- 1 teaspoon onion powder
- Salt and pepper to taste
- 1/2 teaspoon dried oregano

Yield: 4 servings | **Prep time**: 15 minutes | **Cook time**: 1 hours

Directions:

1. Preheat the oven to 375°F (190°C). In a large bowl, mix together the ground turkey, bell peppers, almond flour, egg, tomato paste, garlic powder, onion powder, salt, pepper, and oregano until well combined.
2. Transfer the mixture to a loaf pan lined with parchment paper or lightly greased.
3. Bake in the preheated oven for about 1 hour or until the meatloaf is cooked through and reaches an internal temperature of 165°F (74°C).
4. Let the meatloaf rest for 10 minutes before slicing. Serve warm.

Nutritional Information (per serving): 250 calories, 25g protein, 8g carbohydrates, 12g fat, 2g fiber, 80mg cholesterol, 300mg sodium, 400mg potassium.

Balsamic Glazed Steak Rolls Filled with Vegetables

Ingredients:

- 1 lb flank steak, thinly sliced
- 2 tablespoons olive oil
- 2 bell peppers, thinly sliced
- 1 zucchini, thinly sliced
- 1 carrot, thinly sliced
- 1/2 onion, thinly sliced
- Salt and pepper to taste
- 3 tablespoons balsamic vinegar
- 1 tablespoon soy sauce
- 1 garlic clove, minced
- Fresh herbs (optional) for garnish

Yield: 4 servings | **Prep time**: 20 minutes | **Cook time**: 15 minutes

Directions:

1. Lay out the flank steak slices and season both sides with salt and pepper.
2. In the center of each steak slice, place a few slices of bell pepper, zucchini, carrot, and onion. Roll up the steak around the vegetables and secure with a toothpick.
3. Heat olive oil in a skillet over medium-high heat. Add the steak rolls, searing on all sides until browned, about 2 minutes per side.
4. In a small bowl, mix balsamic vinegar, soy sauce, and minced garlic. Pour this mixture over the steak rolls in the skillet. Reduce heat to medium-low, cover, and cook for about 10 minutes, or until the vegetables are tender.
5. Serve the steak rolls drizzled with the balsamic glaze from the skillet and garnished with fresh herbs, if desired.

Nutritional Information (per serving): 300 calories, 25g protein, 12g carbohydrates, 15g fat, 3g fiber, 50mg cholesterol, 500mg sodium, 400mg potassium.

Herb-Crusted Pork Tenderloin

Ingredients:

- 1 pork tenderloin (approximately 1 to 1.5 pounds)
- 2 tablespoons olive oil
- 2 cloves garlic, minced
- 1 tablespoon fresh rosemary, chopped
- 1 tablespoon fresh thyme, chopped
- Salt and pepper, to taste

Yield: 4 servings | **Prep time**: 15 minutes | **Cook time**: 25 minutes

Directions:

1. Preheat your oven to 400°F (204°C).
2. In a small bowl, mix the olive oil, garlic, rosemary, thyme, salt, and pepper.
3. Rub the herb mixture all over the pork tenderloin, ensuring it's evenly coated.
4. Place the tenderloin in a roasting pan or on a baking sheet.
5. Roast in the preheated oven for 25 minutes, or until the internal temperature reaches 145°F (63°C).
6. Let the pork rest for 5 minutes before slicing and serving.

Nutritional Information (per serving): 220 calories, 25g protein, 2g carbohydrates, 12g fat, 1g fiber, 75mg cholesterol, 220mg sodium, 400mg potassium.

Grilled Chicken Breast with Herbs and Lemon

Yield: 4 servings | **Prep time**: 10 minutes | **Cook time**: 15 minutes

Ingredients:
- 4 chicken breasts (about 6 ounces each)
- 2 tablespoons olive oil
- 1 lemon (juice and zest)
- 2 garlic cloves, minced
- 1 tablespoon fresh rosemary, chopped
- 1 tablespoon fresh thyme, chopped
- Salt and pepper to taste

Directions:
1. Preheat the grill to medium-high heat.
2. In a small bowl, mix olive oil, lemon juice and zest, minced garlic, chopped rosemary, thyme, salt, and pepper.
3. Brush the chicken breasts with the herb mixture.
4. Grill the chicken breasts for about 7-8 minutes per side, or until fully cooked.
5. Let the chicken rest for a few minutes before serving.

Nutritional Information (per serving): 260 calories, 32g protein, 2g carbohydrates, 12g fat, 0g fiber, varies cholesterol, varies sodium, varies potassium.

Turkey Meatballs in a Tomato Basil Sauce

Ingredients:

- 1 lb ground turkey
- 1/4 cup breadcrumbs
- 1/4 cup grated Parmesan cheese
- 1 large egg
- 2 cloves garlic, minced
- 1/2 teaspoon salt
- 1/4 teaspoon black pepper
- 1 tablespoon olive oil
- 2 cups tomato basil sauce (store-bought or homemade)
- Fresh basil leaves, for garnish

Yield: 4 servings | **Prep time**: 20 minutes | **Cook time**: 30 minutes

Directions:

1. In a large bowl, mix together the ground turkey, breadcrumbs, Parmesan cheese, egg, garlic, salt, and pepper until well combined. Form the mixture into 12-16 meatballs.
2. Heat olive oil in a large skillet over medium heat. Add meatballs and cook, turning occasionally, until browned on all sides, about 5-7 minutes.
3. Pour the tomato basil sauce over the meatballs in the skillet. Cover and simmer on low heat for 20-25 minutes, or until the meatballs are cooked through.
4. Garnish with fresh basil leaves before serving. Serve hot over cooked pasta or with a side of bread.

Nutritional Information (per serving): 310 calories, 27g protein, 12g carbohydrates, 17g fat, 2g fiber, 105mg cholesterol, 720mg sodium, 410mg potassium.

Buffalo Chicken Lettuce Wraps

🍴 **Yield**: 4 servings | ⚖️ **Prep time**: 20 minutes | ⏰ **Cook time**: 10 minutes

Ingredients:

- 1 lb boneless, skinless chicken breasts, cooked and shredded
- 1/3 cup buffalo sauce
- 1 cup shredded carrots
- 1 cup diced celery
- 1/2 cup blue cheese crumbles
- 8 large iceberg or butter lettuce leaves
- 1/4 cup Greek yogurt ranch dressing

Directions:

1. In a large bowl, combine the shredded chicken with buffalo sauce until evenly coated.
2. Mix in the shredded carrots and diced celery.
3. Spoon the chicken mixture into the center of each lettuce leaf.
4. Sprinkle blue cheese crumbles over the top of the chicken.
5. Drizzle each wrap with Greek yogurt ranch dressing before serving.

Nutritional Information (per serving): 250 calories, 28g protein, 8g carbohydrates, 12g fat, 3g fiber, 75mg cholesterol, 690mg sodium, 370mg potassium.

Chicken Parmesan over Zucchini Noodles

Ingredients:

- 4 medium-sized chicken breasts, pounded to even thickness
- Salt and pepper, to taste
- 1 cup almond flour
- 2 large eggs, beaten
- 1 cup sugar-free marinara sauce
- 1 cup shredded mozzarella cheese
- 1/4 cup grated Parmesan cheese
- 2 tablespoons olive oil
- 4 large zucchinis, spiralized into noodles
- 2 cloves garlic, minced
- Fresh basil, for garnish

Yield: 4 servings | **Prep time**: 20 minutes | **Cook time**: 30 minutes

Directions:

1. Season the chicken breasts with salt and pepper. Dredge in almond flour, dip in beaten eggs, and coat again in almond flour.
2. Heat olive oil in a large skillet over medium heat. Add chicken and cook until golden brown on both sides and cooked through, about 5-7 minutes per side. Remove chicken and set aside.
3. In the same skillet, add the minced garlic and sauté for 1 minute. Add the spiralized zucchini noodles and cook for 2-3 minutes until just tender.
4. Pour the marinara sauce over the cooked chicken breasts and top each with mozzarella and Parmesan cheese. Broil in the oven for 2-3 minutes, or until the cheese is bubbly and slightly golden.
5. Serve the chicken parmesan over a bed of zucchini noodles. Garnish with fresh basil before serving.

Nutritional Information (per serving): 450 calories, 38g protein, 14g carbohydrates, 27g fat, 4g fiber, 160mg cholesterol, 600mg sodium, 800mg potassium.

Duck Breast with Orange and Balsamic Reduction

Ingredients:

- 4 duck breasts, skin scored
- Salt and freshly ground black pepper, to taste
- 2 oranges, zested and juiced
- 1/2 cup balsamic vinegar
- 1 tablespoon honey
- 1 sprig of fresh thyme
- 1 tablespoon unsalted butter

Yield: 4 servings | **Prep time**: 15 minutes | **Cook time**: 20 minutes

Directions:

1. Preheat the oven to 400°F (200°C). Season the duck breasts with salt and pepper.
2. Place the duck breasts, skin-side down, in a cold skillet. Turn the heat to medium-high and cook until the skin is golden and crisp about 6-8 minutes. Flip the breasts over and cook for an additional 2 minutes.
3. Transfer the duck breasts to a baking dish, skin-side up, and roast in the preheated oven for 6-8 minutes for medium-rare. Remove from the oven, cover loosely with foil, and let rest for 5 minutes.
4. For the reduction, pour out excess fat from the skillet, leaving about a tablespoon. Add the orange juice, zest, balsamic vinegar, honey, and thyme to the skillet. Bring to a boil, then reduce the heat and simmer until the sauce has thickened and reduced by half, about 10-15 minutes. Remove the thyme sprig and whisk in the butter until the sauce is glossy.
5. Slice the duck breasts and serve with the orange and balsamic reduction drizzled over the top.

Nutritional Information (per serving): 350 calories, 30g protein, 15g carbohydrates, 18g fat, 1g fiber, 100mg cholesterol, 200mg sodium, 400mg potassium.

Oven-Baked Chicken Fajitas

Ingredients:

- 1 pound boneless, skinless chicken breasts, thinly sliced
- 1 bell pepper, sliced (any color)
- 1 onion, sliced
- 2 tablespoons olive oil
- 1 tablespoon chili powder
- 2 teaspoons cumin
- 1/2 teaspoon garlic powder
- 1/2 teaspoon paprika
- Salt and pepper to taste
- 8 small flour tortillas
- Optional for serving: shredded cheese, sour cream, salsa, lime wedges

Yield: 4 servings | **Prep time**: 15 minutes | **Cook time**: 25 minutes

Directions:

1. Preheat your oven to 400°F (200°C). In a large bowl, combine chicken, bell pepper, and onion. Drizzle with olive oil and sprinkle with chili powder, cumin, garlic powder, paprika, salt, and pepper. Toss to evenly coat.
2. Spread the chicken and vegetable mixture on a baking sheet in a single layer. Bake for 25 minutes, or until the chicken is thoroughly cooked and vegetables are tender.
3. Warm the flour tortillas according to the package instructions.
4. Spoon the chicken and vegetables evenly among the tortillas. Serve with optional toppings like shredded cheese, sour cream, salsa, and lime wedges if desired.

Nutritional Information (per serving): 300 calories, 28g protein, 15g carbohydrates, 12g fat, 3g fiber, 65mg cholesterol, 480mg sodium, 470mg potassium.

Turkey Stuffed Zucchini Boats

Ingredients:

- 4 medium zucchinis, halved lengthwise
- 1 pound ground turkey
- 1 small onion, finely chopped
- 2 cloves garlic, minced
- 1 cup tomato sauce
- 1 teaspoon dried oregano
- 1 teaspoon dried basil
- Salt and pepper, to taste
- 1/2 cup shredded mozzarella cheese
- 1/4 cup grated Parmesan cheese
- 2 tablespoons olive oil
- Fresh parsley, chopped for garnish

Yield: 4 servings | **Prep time**: 20 minutes | **Cook time**: 25 minutes

Directions:

1. Preheat oven to 375°F (190°C). Scoop out centers of zucchini halves to create boats, leaving a 1/4 inch shell. Brush with olive oil, season with salt and pepper, and place on a baking sheet.
2. In a skillet over medium heat, cook ground turkey, onion, and garlic until turkey is browned and onions are soft. Drain any excess fat.
3. Stir in tomato sauce, oregano, basil, salt, and pepper. Simmer for 5 minutes.
4. Fill zucchini boats with turkey mixture, top with cheeses.
5. Bake for 20-25 minutes until zucchini is tender and cheese is melted.
6. Garnish with parsley before serving.

Nutritional Information (per serving): 350 calories, 28g protein, 15g carbohydrates, 20g fat, 3g fiber, 80mg cholesterol, 500mg sodium, 700mg potassium.

Rosemary Garlic Roast Chicken

Ingredients:

- 1 whole chicken (about 4-5 pounds)
- 4 tablespoons olive oil
- 5 cloves garlic, minced
- 2 tablespoons fresh rosemary, chopped
- 1 lemon, halved
- Salt, to taste
- Black pepper, to taste
- 2 onions, quartered
- 1 lb of baby potatoes, halved
- 1 cup chicken broth

Yield: 4 servings | **Prep time**: 20 minutes | **Cook time**: 1 hour 30 minutes

Directions:

1. Preheat the oven to 375°F (190°C).
2. In a small bowl, mix olive oil, minced garlic, chopped rosemary, salt, and black pepper to create a marinade.
3. Rub the chicken inside and out with the marinade. Place lemon halves inside the chicken cavity.
4. Arrange onions and potatoes in a roasting pan and place the chicken on top. Pour chicken broth into the pan to help keep the chicken moist while cooking.
5. Roast in the preheated oven for about 1 hour and 30 minutes, or until the chicken is golden brown and the internal temperature reaches 165°F (74°C).
6. Let the chicken rest for 10 minutes before carving. Serve with roasted onions and potatoes.

Nutritional Information (per serving): 650 calories, 55g protein, 30g carbohydrates, 35g fat, 5g fiber, 150mg cholesterol, 400mg sodium, 800mg potassium.

Moroccan Chicken Tagine with Olives and Lemons

Ingredients:

- 4 skinless, boneless chicken breasts, cut into chunks
- 2 tablespoons olive oil
- 1 large onion, finely chopped
- 2 garlic cloves, minced
- 1 teaspoon ground cumin
- 1 teaspoon ground ginger
- 1 teaspoon turmeric
- 1/2 teaspoon ground cinnamon
- 1 cup low-sodium chicken broth
- 1 can (14 oz) no-salt-added diced tomatoes, undrained
- 1 cup green olives, pitted
- 2 preserved lemons, thinly sliced
- Salt and pepper, to taste
- Fresh cilantro and flat-leaf parsley, chopped for garnish

Yield: 4 servings | **Prep time**: 20 minutes | **Cook time**: 60 minutes

Directions:

1. Heat olive oil in a tagine or a large, heavy-bottomed pot over medium heat. Add onion and garlic, sauté until softened.
2. Add chicken pieces to the pot, season with salt, pepper, cumin, ginger, turmeric, and cinnamon. Cook until the chicken is browned on all sides.
3. Pour in chicken broth and diced tomatoes. Bring to a simmer, then reduce heat to low, cover, and cook for 45 minutes.
4. Add olives and preserved lemons to the tagine, cover, and cook for an additional 15 minutes.
5. Check the seasoning and adjust with salt and pepper as needed. Garnish with chopped cilantro and parsley before serving.

Nutritional Information (per serving): 350 calories, 28g protein, 15g carbohydrates, 18g fat, 4g fiber, 75mg cholesterol, 550mg sodium, 700mg potassium.

Turkey Meatloaf with Sun-dried Tomatoes and Feta

Ingredients:

- 1 1/2 pounds ground turkey (lean)
- 1/2 cup sun-dried tomatoes, chopped
- 1/2 cup feta cheese, crumbled
- 1/4 cup onions, finely chopped
- 2 cloves garlic, minced
- 1/4 cup fresh parsley, chopped
- 1 egg, lightly beaten
- 1/2 cup almond flour
- 1 tsp dried oregano
- Salt and pepper to taste
- 1/4 cup low-sodium chicken broth (for moisture)

Yield: 4 servings | **Prep time**: 20 minutes | **Cook time**: 55 minutes

Directions:

1. Preheat oven to 375°F (190°C).
2. In a large bowl, combine ground turkey, sun-dried tomatoes, feta cheese, onions, garlic, parsley, egg, almond flour, oregano, salt, and pepper. Mix until well combined.
3. Transfer the mixture into a loaf pan. Pour chicken broth over the top to ensure the meatloaf remains moist while cooking.
4. Bake in the preheated oven for about 55 minutes or until the meatloaf is cooked through.
5. Let the meatloaf rest for 10 minutes before slicing. Serve warm.

Nutritional Information (per serving): 350 calories, 38g protein, 10g carbohydrates, 18g fat, 2g fiber, 120mg cholesterol, 400mg sodium.

Chicken Piccata with Capers and Spinach

Ingredients:

- 4 boneless, skinless chicken breasts, pounded to even thickness
- Salt and pepper to taste
- 1/2 cup almond flour (for dredging)
- 2 tablespoons olive oil
- 1/4 cup lemon juice
- 1/2 cup low-sodium chicken broth
- 2 tablespoons capers, rinsed
- 2 cups fresh spinach
- 1 tablespoon fresh parsley, chopped (for garnish)
- Lemon slices (for garnish)

Yield: 4 servings | **Prep time**: 15 minutes | **Cook time**: 20 minutes

Directions:

1. Season the chicken breasts with salt and pepper. Dredge lightly in almond flour, shaking off any excess.
2. In a skillet, heat olive oil over medium-high. Cook chicken until golden and done, about 4-5 minutes per side. Remove and set aside.
3. Add lemon juice, broth, and capers to the skillet; simmer 2 minutes.
4. Return chicken to the skillet, add spinach, and cook until spinach wilts and sauce thickens, about 3-4 minutes.
5. Garnish with parsley and lemon slices to serve.

Nutritional Information (per serving): 300 calories, 28g protein, 8g carbohydrates, 18g fat, 2g fiber, 75mg cholesterol, 350mg sodium, 500mg potassium.

Chicken Alfredo with Shirataki Noodle

Ingredients:
- 1 pound chicken breast, thinly sliced
- 2 packages (7 ounces each) shirataki noodles, rinsed and drained
- 1 tablespoon olive oil
- 2 cloves garlic, minced
- 1 cup low-fat cream cheese
- 1/2 cup grated Parmesan cheese
- 1 cup unsweetened almond milk
- Salt and pepper to taste
- 1 tablespoon chopped fresh parsley for garnish
- 1 teaspoon lemon zest (optional)

Yield: 4 servings | **Prep time**: 15 minutes | **Cook time**: 20 minutes

Directions:

1. Heat the olive oil in a large skillet over medium heat. Add the garlic and sauté until fragrant, about 1 minute.
2. Add the chicken to the skillet and season with salt and pepper. Cook until the chicken is fully cooked through, about 6-8 minutes per side. Remove the chicken from the skillet and set aside.
3. In the same skillet, add the almond milk and cream cheese. Cook over medium heat, stirring until the cream cheese is melted and the sauce is smooth.
4. Stir in the Parmesan cheese until melted and the sauce is creamy. Adjust the seasoning with salt and pepper.
5. Add the shirataki noodles to the skillet, tossing to coat in the Alfredo sauce. Cook until the noodles are heated through, about 3-5 minutes.
6. Slice the cooked chicken and lay it on top of the noodles. Garnish with chopped parsley and lemon zest if desired.

Nutritional Information (per serving): 350 calories, 38g protein, 8g carbohydrates, 18g fat, 2g fiber, 105mg cholesterol, 690mg sodium, 500mg potassium.

Shrimp and Broccoli Stir-Fry with Garlic Sauce

Yield: 4 servings | **Prep time**: 15 minutes | **Cook time**: 10 minutes

Ingredients:

- 1 lb large shrimp, peeled and deveined
- 4 cups broccoli florets
- 2 tablespoons olive oil
- 3 garlic cloves, minced
- 2 tablespoons soy sauce (low sodium)
- 1 tablespoon oyster sauce (optional for added flavor)
- 1 teaspoon sesame oil
- 1 tablespoon grated ginger
- Red pepper flakes to taste (optional for spice)
- Salt and pepper to taste
- 1 tablespoon cornstarch mixed with 2 tablespoons water (for thickening)
- Sesame seeds and sliced green onions for garnish

Directions:

1. Heat olive oil in a large skillet over medium-high heat. Add garlic and ginger, stir-fry for 30 seconds.
2. Add shrimp to the skillet, season with a pinch of salt and pepper, and stir-fry until shrimp are pink and opaque, about 2-3 minutes. Remove shrimp from skillet and set aside.
3. In the same skillet, add broccoli florets, soy sauce, oyster sauce (if using), and sesame oil. Stir well to combine. Cover and let steam until broccoli is tender-crisp, about 3-4 minutes.
4. Return shrimp to the skillet. Add the cornstarch and water mixture to thicken the sauce. Stir everything together and cook for another 2 minutes.
5. Sprinkle with red pepper flakes (if using), sesame seeds, and green onions before serving.

Nutritional Information (per serving): 220 calories, 24g protein, 8g carbohydrates, 10g fat, 3g fiber, 180mg cholesterol, 600mg sodium, 300mg potassium.

Mussels in a White Wine Tomato Broth

Ingredients:

- 2 pounds fresh mussels, cleaned and debearded
- 1 tablespoon olive oil
- 3 cloves garlic, minced
- 1 small onion, finely chopped
- 1 cup white wine
- 1 can (14 ounces) diced tomatoes, undrained
- 1 tablespoon fresh parsley, chopped
- 1 tablespoon fresh basil, chopped
- Salt and pepper, to taste

Yield: 4 servings | **Prep time**: 15 minutes | **Cook time**: 20 minutes

Directions:

1. In a large pot, heat olive oil over medium heat. Add garlic and onion, and sauté until softened, about 5 minutes.
2. Pour in the white wine and bring to a simmer. Add the diced tomatoes, including their juice, and bring to a simmer again.
3. Add the mussels to the pot. Cover and cook over medium heat until the mussels have opened, about 10 minutes. Discard any mussels that do not open.
4. Stir in the chopped parsley and basil. Season with salt and pepper to taste.
5. Serve the mussels and broth in deep bowls, ensuring each serving gets a generous amount of the tomato broth.

Nutritional Information (per serving): 300 calories, 22g protein, 12g carbohydrates, 10g fat, 1g fiber, 50mg cholesterol, 400mg sodium, 500mg potassium.

Baked Cod with Tomato and Basil

Yield: 4 servings | **Prep time**: 15 min. | **Cook time**: 20 min.

Ingredients:

- 4 cod fillets (about 6 ounces each)
- 2 tablespoons olive oil
- Salt and pepper, to taste
- 2 tomatoes, sliced
- 1/4 cup fresh basil leaves, chopped
- 2 garlic cloves, minced
- 1 lemon, sliced (for garnish)

Directions:

1. Preheat your oven to 400°F (200°C). Lightly oil a baking dish.
2. Place cod fillets in the prepared baking dish. Season with salt and pepper.
3. Top each fillet with tomato slices, minced garlic, and basil. Drizzle with olive oil.
4. Bake in the preheated oven until fish flakes easily with a fork, about 15-20 minutes.
5. Garnish with lemon slices before serving.

Nutritional Information *(per serving): 200 calories, 23g protein, 5g carbohydrates, 10g fat, 1g fiber, 60mg cholesterol, 300mg sodium, 500mg potassium*

Seafood Paella with Cauliflower Rice

Yield: 4 servings | **Prep time**: 20 min. | **Cook time**: 30 min.

Ingredients:

- 4 cups of cauliflower rice
- 1 lb mixed seafood (shrimp, mussels, and squid)
- 1 large onion, diced
- 2 cloves garlic, minced
- 1 bell pepper, sliced
- 1/2 cup diced tomatoes
- 1/2 teaspoon saffron threads
- 1 teaspoon smoked paprika
- 2 tablespoons olive oil
- Salt and pepper to taste
- Fresh parsley, chopped for garnish
- Lemon wedges for serving

Directions:

1. Heat olive oil in a large skillet over medium heat. Add onion, garlic, and bell pepper. Cook until softened.
2. Stir in cauliflower rice, tomatoes, saffron, and smoked paprika. Season with salt and pepper.
3. Add the mixed seafood to the skillet, gently folding it into the cauliflower mixture. Cover and cook for about 15-20 minutes, or until seafood is cooked through.
4. Garnish with fresh parsley and serve with lemon wedges on the side.

Nutritional Information *(per serving): 300 calories, 25g protein, 15g carbohydrates, 12g fat, 4g fiber, 120mg cholesterol, 500mg sodium, 650mg potassium.*

Grilled Salmon with Lemon Dill Sauce

Ingredients:

- 4 salmon fillets (6 ounces each)
- 2 tablespoons olive oil
- Salt and pepper, to taste
- 1 lemon, juiced and zested
- 2 tablespoons fresh dill, chopped
- 1 clove garlic, minced
- 1/2 cup Greek yogurt
- 1 teaspoon Dijon mustard

Yield: 4 servings | **Prep time**: 15 minutes | **Cook time**: 10 minutes

Directions:

1. Preheat your grill to medium-high heat.
2. Rub the salmon fillets with olive oil and season with salt and pepper.
3. Grill the salmon, skin side down, for about 5-6 minutes. Flip carefully and grill for an additional 3-4 minutes, or until the salmon is cooked through and flakes easily with a fork.
4. In a small bowl, mix the lemon juice and zest, fresh dill, minced garlic, Greek yogurt, and Dijon mustard to create the sauce.
5. Serve the grilled salmon with a generous drizzle of the lemon dill sauce.

Nutritional Information (per serving): 320 calories, 34g protein, 4g carbohydrates, 18g fat, 1g fiber, 90mg cholesterol 200mg sodium, 800mg potassium.

Tuna Nicoise Salad

Ingredients:

- 4 fresh tuna steaks (about 6 ounces each) or 2 cans of tuna in water, drained
- 8 small new potatoes, boiled until tender and cooled
- 2 large eggs, hard-boiled, peeled, and quartered
- 1 cup green beans, trimmed and blanched
- 1/2 cup black olives, pitted
- 4 medium tomatoes, cut into wedges
- Mixed salad greens (such as romaine or baby spinach)

For the dressing:

- 1/4 cup olive oil
- 2 tablespoons red wine vinegar
- 1 tablespoon Dijon mustard
- 1 small garlic clove, minced
- Salt and pepper, to taste
- Fresh herbs (such as parsley or basil), for garnish

Yield: 4 servings | **Prep time**: 20 minutes | **Cook time**: 10 minutes

Directions:

1. If using fresh tuna, season the tuna steaks with salt and pepper and grill over high heat for 2-3 minutes on each side for medium-rare. Let it rest for a few minutes, then slice thinly. If using canned tuna, simply prepare the tuna by flaking it with a fork.
2. Arrange the mixed salad greens on a large platter. Distribute the potatoes, green beans, tomatoes, olives, and eggs evenly over the greens.
3. In a small bowl, whisk together the olive oil, red wine vinegar, Dijon mustard, minced garlic, salt, and pepper to create the dressing.
4. Drizzle the dressing over the salad and gently toss to combine.
5. Top the salad with the sliced tuna or flaked canned tuna.
6. Garnish with fresh herbs before serving.

Nutritional Information (per serving): 350 calories, 28g protein, 20g carbohydrates, 18g fat, 4g fiber, 60mg cholesterol, 400mg sodium, 750mg potassium.

Crab Cakes with Avocado Aioli (Using Almond Flour)

Ingredients:

- 1 pound lump crab meat, picked over for shells
- 1 cup almond flour, plus extra for coating
- 2 green onions, finely chopped
- 1 egg, beaten
- 2 tablespoons mayonnaise (look for a low-carb, sugar-free option)
- 1 teaspoon Dijon mustard
- 1/2 teaspoon paprika
- Zest of 1 lemon
- Salt and pepper, to taste
- 2 tablespoons olive oil, for frying

For the Avocado Aioli:

- 1 ripe avocado
- 1/4 cup mayonnaise
- 1 clove garlic, minced
- Juice of 1/2 lemon
- Salt and pepper, to taste

Yield: 4 servings | **Prep time**: 20 minutes | **Cook time**: 10 minutes

Directions:

1. In a large bowl, mix together crab meat, almond flour, green onions, egg, mayonnaise, Dijon mustard, paprika, lemon zest, salt, and pepper. Form the mixture into patties.
2. Place extra almond flour on a plate. Lightly coat each crab cake in almond flour.
3. Heat olive oil in a large skillet over medium heat. Fry crab cakes for about 4-5 minutes on each side, or until golden brown and crispy.
4. For the aioli, blend together avocado, mayonnaise, garlic, lemon juice, salt, and pepper until smooth.
5. Serve crab cakes hot with a dollop of avocado aioli on top or on the side.

Nutritional Information (per serving): 350 calories, 25g protein, 10g carbohydrates, 25g fat, 5g fiber, 125mg cholesterol, 700mg sodium, 300mg potassium.

Seared Scallops with Cauliflower Puree

Yield: 4 servings | **Prep time**: 15 min. | **Cook time**: 20 min.

Ingredients:
- 1 lb sea scallops
- 1 head cauliflower, cut into florets
- 2 tablespoons olive oil
- 1 garlic clove, minced
- 1/2 cup unsweetened almond milk
- Salt and pepper, to taste
- Fresh herbs for garnish (optional)

Directions:
1. Preheat your pan over medium-high heat and add 1 tablespoon olive oil. Season scallops with salt and pepper, then sear for about 2 minutes on each side until golden brown. Remove from the pan and set aside.
2. Steam the cauliflower until very tender, then blend in a food processor with almond milk, garlic, salt, and pepper until smooth.
3. Reheat the puree if needed, and adjust seasoning to taste.
4. Serve the scallops over a bed of cauliflower puree and garnish with fresh herbs if desired.

Nutritional Information (per serving): 250 calories, 24g protein, 8g carbohydrates, 14g fat, 3g fiber, 55mg cholesterol, 320mg sodium, 500mg potassium

Grilled Tilapia with Mango Salsa

Yield: 4 servings | **Prep time**: 20 min. | **Cook time**: 10 min.

Ingredients:
- 4 tilapia fillets
- 2 tablespoons olive oil
- Salt and pepper to taste
- 1 ripe mango, diced
- 1/2 red bell pepper, diced
- 1/4 cup red onion, finely chopped
- 1 small jalapeño, seeded and minced (optional)
- Juice of 1 lime
- 2 tablespoons fresh cilantro, chopped
- Salt to taste

Directions:
1. Preheat grill to medium-high heat.
2. Brush tilapia fillets with olive oil and season with salt and pepper.
3. Grill tilapia for 3-5 minutes on each side, or until fish flakes easily with a fork.
4. In a medium bowl, combine mango, red bell pepper, red onion, jalapeño (if using), lime juice, and cilantro. Season with salt to taste and mix well.
5. Serve the grilled tilapia topped with mango salsa.

Nutritional Information (per serving): 250 calories, 35g protein, 15g carbohydrates, 7g fat, 2g fiber, 85mg cholesterol, 150mg sodium, 500mg potassium.

Spicy Garlic Lime Shrimp

Ingredients:

- 1 lb large shrimp, peeled and deveined
- 2 tablespoons olive oil
- 4 garlic cloves, minced
- 1 teaspoon red pepper flakes (adjust to taste)
- Zest and juice of 1 lime
- 1/4 cup chopped cilantro
- Salt and pepper, to taste

Yield: 4 servings | **Prep time**: 10 minutes | **Cook time**: 10 minutes

Directions:

1. In a large skillet, heat the olive oil over medium-high heat. Add the garlic and red pepper flakes, cooking until fragrant, about 1 minute.
2. Add the shrimp to the skillet, seasoning with salt and pepper. Cook until the shrimp turn pink and opaque, about 2-3 minutes per side.
3. Remove the skillet from heat. Stir in the lime zest, lime juice, and chopped cilantro, tossing to coat the shrimp evenly.
4. Serve immediately, garnished with lime wedges if desired.

Nutritional Information *(per serving)*: *200 calories, 24g protein, 3g carbohydrates, 10g fat, 0g fiber, 180mg cholesterol, 300mg sodium, 200mg potassium.*

Almond-Crusted Eggplant Parmesan

🍴   ⚖️   ⏰

Yield: 4 servings | **Prep time**: 20 minutes | **Cook time**: 30 minutes

Ingredients:

- 2 medium eggplants, sliced into 1/2 inch rounds
- 2 eggs, beaten
- 1 cup almond flour
- 1 tablespoon Italian seasoning
- Salt and pepper to taste
- 2 cups low-sugar marinara sauce
- 1 cup shredded mozzarella cheese (low-fat)
- 1/4 cup grated Parmesan cheese
- Fresh basil leaves for garnish

Directions:

1. Preheat oven to 375°F (190°C) and line a baking sheet with parchment paper.
2. Season almond flour with Italian seasoning, salt, and pepper in a shallow dish.
3. Dip eggplant slices in beaten eggs, then dredge in seasoned almond flour to coat both sides; place on prepared baking sheet.
4. Bake in preheated oven for 20 minutes, flipping halfway through, until eggplant is golden and slightly crispy.
5. Spread a thin layer of marinara sauce on the bottom of a baking dish. Layer baked eggplant slices, more sauce, mozzarella, and Parmesan cheese. Repeat layers until all ingredients are used.
6. Bake for an additional 10 minutes, or until cheese is melted and bubbly.
7. Garnish with fresh basil before serving.

Nutritional Information *(per serving): 300 calories, 15g protein, 15g carbohydrates, 18g fat, 6g fiber, 60 cholesterol, varies sodium, 500 potassium.*

Cauliflower Steak with Chimichurri Sauce

Ingredients:

- 2 large heads of cauliflower
- 2 tablespoons olive oil
- Salt and pepper, to taste

For the Chimichurri Sauce:

- 1 cup fresh parsley, finely chopped
- 1/4 cup fresh cilantro, finely chopped
- 1/2 cup olive oil
- 1/4 cup red wine vinegar
- 3 garlic cloves, minced
- 1 teaspoon red pepper flakes
- Salt and pepper, to tast

Yield: 4 servings | **Prep time**: 10 minutes | **Cook time**: 25 minutes

Directions:

1. Preheat your oven to 400°F (200°C).
2. Remove the leaves from the cauliflower and cut the stem slightly, ensuring the head stays intact. Slice the cauliflower into 1-inch thick steaks. Depending on the size, you should get about 2-3 steaks per head.
3. Brush each cauliflower steak with olive oil and season with salt and pepper. Place on a baking sheet.
4. Roast in the preheated oven for about 25 minutes, turning halfway through, until golden brown and tender.
5. While the cauliflower is roasting, prepare the chimichurri sauce. In a bowl, combine parsley, cilantro, olive oil, red wine vinegar, garlic, red pepper flakes, salt, and pepper. Mix well.
6. Once the cauliflower steaks are done, serve them with a generous drizzle of chimichurri sauce.

Nutritional Information (per serving): 250 calories, 3g protein, 10g carbohydrates, 22g fat, 4g fiber, 0mg cholesterol, 200mg sodium, 600mg potassium.

Stuffed Acorn Squash with Quinoa and Cranberries

Yield: 4 servings | **Prep time**: 20 min. | **Cook time**: 45 min.

Ingredients:

- 2 acorn squashes, halved and seeds removed
- 1 cup quinoa, rinsed
- 2 cups vegetable broth
- 1/2 cup dried cranberries
- 1/2 cup chopped pecans
- 1 tablespoon olive oil
- 1/2 teaspoon cinnamon
- Salt and pepper to taste
- Fresh parsley, chopped (for garnish)

Directions:

1. Preheat your oven to 375°F (190°C). Brush the inside of each acorn squash half with olive oil and season with salt and pepper. Place cut side down on a baking sheet and roast for about 25-30 minutes until tender.
2. While the squash is roasting, cook the quinoa in vegetable broth according to package instructions. Once cooked, fluff with a fork and set aside.
3. In a large bowl, mix the cooked quinoa with dried cranberries, chopped pecans, cinnamon, and additional salt and pepper to taste.
4. Once the acorn squash is tender, remove from the oven, flip them over, and stuff with the quinoa mixture. Return to the oven and bake for an additional 15 minutes.
5. Garnish with fresh parsley before serving.

Nutritional Information (per serving): 310 calories, 6g protein, 50g carbohydrates, 10g fat, 8g fiber, 0mg cholesterol, 150mg sodium, 700mg potassium

Zucchini Noodles with Avocado Pesto

Yield: 4 servings | **Prep time**: 15 min. | **Cook time**: 0 min.

Ingredients:

- 4 large zucchinis, spiralized into noodles
- 2 ripe avocados, pitted and peeled
- 1/2 cup fresh basil leaves
- 2 cloves garlic
- 2 tablespoons lemon juice
- 1/4 cup extra-virgin olive oil
- Salt and pepper, to taste
- Cherry tomatoes and pine nuts, for garnish (optional)

Directions:

1. Place the avocado, basil, garlic, lemon juice, and olive oil in a food processor. Blend until smooth. Season with salt and pepper to taste.
2. Combine the zucchini noodles and avocado pesto in a large bowl. Toss until the noodles are well coated.
3. Serve immediately, garnished with cherry tomatoes and pine nuts if desired.

Nutritional Information (per serving): 250 calories, 4g protein, 12g carbohydrates, 22g fat, 7g fiber, 0mg cholesterol, 20mg sodium, 700mg potassium.

Grilled Portobello Mushrooms with Quinoa Salad

Ingredients:

- 4 large portobello mushroom caps, cleaned and stems removed
- 1 cup quinoa, rinsed
- 2 cups water or vegetable broth
- 1 small red onion, finely chopped
- 1 cucumber, diced
- 1 bell pepper, any color, diced
- 1/4 cup fresh parsley, chopped
- 2 tablespoons olive oil, plus extra for grilling
- Juice of 1 lemon
- Salt and pepper, to taste
- Optional garnishes: feta cheese, cherry tomatoes, avocado slices

Yield: 4 servings | **Prep time**: 15 minutes | **Cook time**: 10 minutes

Directions:

1. In a medium saucepan, bring water or broth to a boil. Add quinoa, reduce heat to low, cover, and simmer for 15 minutes or until all liquid is absorbed. Remove from heat and let stand covered for 5 minutes. Fluff with a fork and allow to cool.
2. Preheat grill to medium-high heat. Brush portobello mushrooms with olive oil and season with salt and pepper. Grill for about 5 minutes per side or until tender.
3. In a large bowl, combine cooled quinoa, red onion, cucumber, bell pepper, and parsley. Drizzle with olive oil and lemon juice, then season with salt and pepper to taste. Toss to combine.
4. Serve grilled portobello mushrooms topped with quinoa salad. Add optional garnishes like feta cheese, cherry tomatoes, or avocado slices if desired.

Nutritional Information (per serving): 250 calories, 8g protein, 35g carbohydrates, 10g fat, 6g fiber, 0mg cholesterol, 200mg sodium, 600mg potassium.

Vegan Black Bean and Sweet Potato Enchiladas

Ingredients:

- 2 medium sweet potatoes, peeled and diced
- 1 can (15 oz) black beans, drained and rinsed
- 1 cup corn (fresh or frozen)
- 2 cups homemade or store-bought enchilada sauce
- 12 corn tortillas
- 1 avocado, diced (for garnish)
- Fresh cilantro, chopped (for garnish)
- Salt and pepper to taste
- 1 teaspoon cumin
- 1 teaspoon paprika
- 2 tablespoons olive oil

Yield: 6 servings | **Prep time**: 25 minutes | **Cook time**: 30 minutes

Directions:

1. Preheat the oven to 375°F (190°C). Toss sweet potatoes with olive oil, cumin, paprika, salt, and pepper. Spread on a baking sheet and roast until tender, about 20 minutes.
2. In a large bowl, mix roasted sweet potatoes, black beans, and corn. Add half a cup of enchilada sauce to the mixture for moisture and flavor.
3. Warm tortillas in the oven or on a skillet to make them pliable. Spoon the mixture into tortillas, roll them up, and place them seam side down in a baking dish.
4. Pour the remaining enchilada sauce over the rolled tortillas, ensuring they are thoroughly coated.
5. Bake in the preheated oven until the sauce bubbles and the edges of the tortillas begin to crisp, about 20 minutes.
6. Garnish with diced avocado and chopped cilantro before serving.

Nutritional Information (per serving): 350 calories, 10g protein, 55g carbohydrates, 8g fat, 15g fiber, 0mg cholesterol, 500mg sodium, 800mg potassium.

Ratatouille with Eggplant, Zucchini, and Tomato

Yield: 6 servings | **Prep time**: 20 min. | **Cook time**: 40 min.

Ingredients:
- 1 large eggplant, cut into cubes
- 2 medium zucchinis, sliced
- 2 large tomatoes, chopped
- 1 bell pepper, any color, chopped
- 1 onion, chopped
- 2 cloves garlic, minced
- 2 tablespoons olive oil
- 1 teaspoon dried thyme
- 1 teaspoon dried basil
- Salt and pepper to taste
- Fresh basil for garnish

Directions:
1. Preheat the oven to 375°F (190°C).
2. In a large baking dish, combine eggplant, zucchinis, tomatoes, bell pepper, onion, and garlic. Drizzle with olive oil and sprinkle with thyme, basil, salt, and pepper. Toss to coat evenly.
3. Bake in the preheated oven for about 40 minutes, stirring halfway through, until vegetables are tender and lightly browned.
4. Garnish with fresh basil before serving.

Nutritional Information (per serving): 120 calories, 3g protein, 18g carbohydrates, 5g fat, 6g fiber, 0mg cholesterol, 150mg sodium, 650mg potassium

Vegan Jambalaya with Brown Rice

Yield: 4 servings | **Prep time**: 20 min. | **Cook time**: 40 min.

Ingredients:
- 1 cup brown rice
- 2 tablespoons olive oil
- 1 medium onion, diced
- 2 cloves garlic, minced
- 1 bell pepper, diced
- 2 stalks celery, diced
- 1 can (14.5 oz) diced tomatoes, undrained
- 1 cup vegetable broth
- 1 teaspoon smoked paprika
- 1/2 teaspoon dried thyme
- 1/2 teaspoon dried oregano
- Salt and pepper to taste
- 1 cup sliced okra (fresh or frozen)
- 1 can (15 oz) red beans, rinsed and drained

Nutritional Information (per serving): 300 calories, 10g protein, 55g carbohydrates, 5g fat, 8g fiber, 0mg cholesterol, 400mg sodium, 600mg

Directions:
1. Cook the brown rice according to package instructions and set aside.
2. In a large skillet or pot, heat the olive oil over medium heat. Add the onion, garlic, bell pepper, and celery, and sauté until the vegetables are softened, about 5-7 minutes.
3. Stir in the diced tomatoes, vegetable broth, smoked paprika, thyme, oregano, salt, and pepper. Bring to a simmer.
4. Add the okra and red beans to the skillet. Cover and simmer for 20 minutes, or until the vegetables are tender.
5. Serve the vegetable and bean mixture over the cooked brown rice. Garnish with green onions and parsley if desired.

Moroccan Stew with Chickpeas and Vegetables

Ingredients:

- 1 tablespoon olive oil
- 1 large onion, chopped
- 2 cloves garlic, minced
- 2 teaspoons ground cumin
- 1 teaspoon ground cinnamon
- 1 teaspoon ground coriander
- 1 can (14.5 oz) diced tomatoes, undrained
- 1 can (15 oz) chickpeas, drained and rinsed
- 2 cups vegetable broth
- 1 cup chopped carrots
- 1 cup chopped zucchini
- 1 cup chopped bell pepper
- 1/2 cup raisins or dried apricots (optional)
- Salt and pepper to taste
- Fresh cilantro, for garnish

Yield: 6 servings | **Prep time**: 15 minutes | **Cook time**: 40 minutes

Directions:

1. Heat olive oil in a large pot over medium heat. Add onion and garlic, cooking until softened, about 5 minutes.
2. Stir in cumin, cinnamon, and coriander, cooking for another minute until fragrant.
3. Add diced tomatoes, chickpeas, vegetable broth, carrots, zucchini, bell pepper, and raisins. Season with salt and pepper.
4. Bring to a boil, then reduce heat and simmer, covered, for 30 minutes, or until vegetables are tender.
5. Serve hot, garnished with fresh cilantro.

Nutritional Information (per serving): 200 calories, 7g protein, 35g carbohydrates, 4g fat, 9g fiber, 0mg cholesterol, 300mg sodium, 600mg potassium.

Vegetable Stir-Fry with Tofu and Low-Sodium Soy Sauce

Ingredients:

- 1 block (14 oz) firm tofu, pressed and cut into cubes
- 2 tablespoons olive oil or sesame oil
- 2 cups broccoli florets
- 1 red bell pepper, sliced
- 1 yellow bell pepper, sliced
- 1 cup snap peas
- 1 carrot, julienned
- 2 cloves garlic, minced
- 1 tablespoon ginger, minced
- 1/4 cup low-sodium soy sauce
- 1 tablespoon rice vinegar
- 1 teaspoon chili flakes (optional)
- Salt and pepper to taste
- 2 green onions, sliced for garnish
- 1 teaspoon sesame seeds for garnish

Yield: 4 servings | **Prep time**: 15 minutes | **Cook time**: 10 minutes

Directions:

1. Heat a large skillet or wok over medium-high heat. Add 1 tablespoon oil and tofu cubes. Cook until golden brown on all sides. Remove tofu from the skillet and set aside.
2. Add the remaining oil to the skillet, then add broccoli, bell peppers, snap peas, and carrot. Stir-fry for about 5 minutes or until vegetables are just tender.
3. Add garlic and ginger to the skillet and cook for an additional minute.
4. Return the tofu to the skillet. Add low-sodium soy sauce and rice vinegar. If using, sprinkle chili flakes. Stir well to combine and heat through for about 2 minutes.
5. Taste and adjust seasoning with salt and pepper. Serve hot, garnished with green onions and sesame seeds.

Nutritional Information (per serving): 220 calories, 12g protein, 18g carbohydrates, 12g fat, 4g fiber, 0mg cholesterol, 500mg sodium, 300mg potassium.

Mini Bell Pepper Nachos

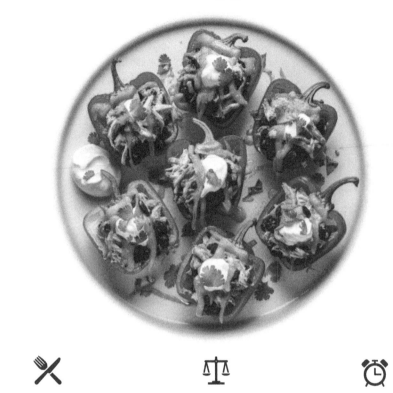

Yield: 4 servings | **Prep time**: 10 minutes | **Cook time**: 15 minutes

Ingredients:

- 1 pound mini bell peppers, halved and seeds removed
- 1 cup cooked and shredded chicken breast
- 1 cup shredded low-fat cheddar cheese
- 1/2 cup black beans, rinsed and drained
- 1/4 cup red onion, finely chopped
- 1/4 cup fresh cilantro, chopped
- 1 avocado, diced
- 1 lime, juiced
- Salt and pepper, to taste
- Greek yogurt or sour cream, for serving
- Salsa, for serving

Directions:

1. Preheat your oven to 375°F (190°C). Arrange the halved mini bell peppers on a baking sheet in a single layer.
2. In a bowl, mix the shredded chicken, black beans, red onion, half of the cilantro, lime juice, salt, and pepper.
3. Spoon the chicken mixture into each bell pepper half and sprinkle with shredded cheese.
4. Bake in the preheated oven for about 15 minutes, or until the cheese is melted and bubbly.
5. Garnish with the remaining cilantro and diced avocado. Serve with Greek yogurt and salsa on the side.

Nutritional Information (per serving): 300 calories, 25g protein, 20g carbohydrates, 15g fat, 6g fiber, 60 cholesterol, 400 sodium, 500 potassium.

Caprese Skewers with Balsamic Reduction

Yield: 4 servings | **Prep time**: 15 min. | **Cook time**: 10 min.

Ingredients:
- 16 cherry tomatoes
- 16 fresh mozzarella balls
- 16 fresh basil leaves
- 2 tablespoons olive oil
- Salt and pepper, to taste
- 1/2 cup balsamic vinegar
- Wooden skewers

Directions:
1. Thread a cherry tomato, a basil leaf, and a mozzarella ball onto a skewer. Repeat until all ingredients are used.
2. Drizzle olive oil over the skewers and season with salt and pepper.
3. For the balsamic reduction, pour balsamic vinegar into a small saucepan and simmer over medium heat until it reduces by half and thickens, about 10 minutes.
4. Drizzle the balsamic reduction over the skewers before serving.

Nutritional Information (per serving): 250 calories, 12g protein, 10g carbohydrates, 18g fat, 1g fiber, 30mg cholesterol, 400mg sodium, 150mg potassium

Cucumber Hummus Bites

Yield: 15 bites | **Prep time**: 10 min. | **Cook time**: 10 min.

Ingredients:
- 1 large cucumber, sliced into ¼- thick rounds
- 1 cup hummus, your choice of flavor
- Paprika, for garnish
- Fresh parsley, finely chopped, for garnish

Directions:

1. Lay cucumber slices on a serving plate.
2. Top each cucumber slice with a generous teaspoon of hummus.
3. Sprinkle a dash of paprika and some chopped parsley on each for garnish.
4. Serve immediately or keep chilled until ready to serve.

Nutritional Information (Estimation per bite): 40 calories, 1g protein, 4g carbohydrates, 2g fat, 1g fiber

Turkey and Spinach Roll-Ups

Yield: 4 servings | **Prep time**: 15 min. | **Cook time**: 15 min.
Ingredients:
- 8 slices of turkey breast (thinly sliced)
- 2 cups fresh spinach leaves
- 1/2 cup low-fat cream cheese, softened
- 1/4 cup roasted red peppers, sliced
- Salt and pepper to taste
- Optional: herbs such as dill or chives for extra flavor

Directions:

1. Lay out the turkey breast slices on a clean surface. Spread a thin layer of cream cheese on each slice.
2. Place a few spinach leaves and slices of roasted red pepper on one end of each turkey slice.
3. Roll up the turkey slices tightly, starting from the end with the fillings. Secure with a toothpick if necessary.
4. Season the roll-ups with salt, pepper, and optional herbs to taste. Serve immediately or chill in the refrigerator before serving.

Nutritional Information (per serving): 150 calories, 20g protein, 5g carbohydrates, 6g fat, 1g fiber, 35mg cholesterol, 400mg sodium.

Eggplant Pizza Bites

Yield: 4 servings | **Prep time**: 15 min. | **Cook time**: 25 min.
Ingredients:
- 1 large eggplant, cut into 1/2-inch thick rounds
- 1 cup low-sodium marinara sauce
- 1 cup shredded low-fat mozzarella cheese
- 1/2 cup chopped fresh basil
- 1/2 cup sliced black olives
- 2 tablespoons olive oil
- Salt and pepper, to taste
- Optional toppings: sliced mushrooms, diced bell peppers, onion slices

Directions:

1. Preheat the oven to 400°F (200°C). Line a baking sheet with parchment paper.
2. Arrange eggplant rounds on the prepared baking sheet. Brush both sides of the eggplant with olive oil and season with salt and pepper.
3. Bake in the preheated oven for 15 minutes, flipping halfway through, until slightly tender.
4. Remove the eggplant from the oven. Top each round with marinara sauce, mozzarella cheese, basil, olives, and any other toppings of your choice.
5. Return to the oven and bake for an additional 10 minutes, or until the cheese is melted and bubbly.
6. Serve hot, garnished with more fresh basil if desired.

Nutritional Information (per serving): 180 calories, 9g protein, 13g carbohydrates, 11g fat, 5g fiber, 20mg cholesterol, 350mg sodium, 400mg potassium

Vegetable Spring Rolls with Peanut Dipping Sauce

Ingredients:

- 8 rice paper wrappers
- 1 cup thinly sliced cabbage
- 1 carrot, julienned
- 1 cucumber, julienned
- 1 bell pepper, julienned
- 1/2 cup fresh cilantro leaves
- 1/2 cup fresh mint leaves

For the Peanut Dipping Sauce:

- 1/4 cup peanut butter
- 2 tablespoons soy sauce (low sodium)
- 1 tablespoon lime juice
- 1 tablespoon honey (or a suitable sugar-free sweetener)
- 2-4 tablespoons water (to adjust consistency)
- 1/2 teaspoon crushed red pepper flakes (optional)

Yield: 4 servings | **Prep time**: 30 minutes | **Cook time**: 0 minutes

Directions:

1. Soften rice paper wrappers by dipping them one at a time in warm water for a few seconds until they are just pliable. Lay them out on a clean, slightly damp cloth.
2. On each wrapper, place an equal amount of cabbage, carrot, cucumber, bell pepper, cilantro, and mint towards the bottom edge of the wrapper.
3. Roll up the wrapper tightly, folding in the sides as you go, to enclose the filling.
4. For the peanut dipping sauce, whisk together peanut butter, soy sauce, lime juice, honey, water, and red pepper flakes until smooth.
5. Serve the spring rolls immediately with the peanut dipping sauce on the side.

Nutritional Information (per serving): 200 calories, 6g protein, 30g carbohydrates, 8g fat, 3g fiber, 0mg cholesterol, 200mg sodium, 350mg potassium.

Zucchini Fritters with Yogurt-Dill Sauce

Ingredients:

For the Fritters:
- 2 large zucchinis, grated
- 2 green onions, finely chopped
- 1 clove garlic, minced
- 2 large eggs, beaten
- 1/2 cup almond flour
- Salt and pepper to taste
- Olive oil for frying

For the Yogurt-Dill Sauce:
- 1 cup Greek yogurt
- 2 tablespoons fresh dill, chopped
- 1 tablespoon lemon juice
- 1 clove garlic, minced
- Salt and pepper to taste

Yield: 4 servings | **Prep time**: 15 minutes | **Cook time**: 10 minutes

Directions:

1. Combine grated zucchini, green onions, garlic, eggs, almond flour, salt, and pepper in a large bowl. Mix until well combined.
2. Heat olive oil in a large skillet over medium heat. Spoon the zucchini mixture into the skillet, flattening to form fritters. Cook until golden brown on both sides, about 4-5 minutes per side.
3. For the sauce, combine Greek yogurt, dill, lemon juice, garlic, salt, and pepper in a small bowl. Mix until smooth.
4. Serve the fritters hot with a dollop of yogurt-dill sauce on top.

Nutritional Information (per serving): Calories: 200, Protein: 12g, Carbohydrates: 10g, Fat: 12g, Fiber: 3g, Cholesterol: 100mg, Sodium: 300mg, Potassium: 400mg.

Smoked Salmon and Cream Cheese Cucumber Bites

Yield: 4 servings | **Prep time**: 15 min. | **Cook time**: 0 min.

Ingredients:

- 1 large cucumber, sliced into rounds
- 4 oz cream cheese, softened
- 4 oz smoked salmon, cut into bite-sized pieces
- Fresh dill for garnish
- Black pepper to taste

Directions:

1. Arrange cucumber slices on a serving platter.
2. Spread a small amount of cream cheese on each cucumber slice.
3. Top each with a piece of smoked salmon.
4. Garnish with fresh dill and a sprinkle of black pepper.
5. Serve immediately or chill until serving.

Nutritional Information (per serving): 120 calories, 8g protein, 4g carbohydrates, 9g fat, 1g fiber, 25mg cholesterol, 250 mg sodium, 175mg potassium.

Greek Yogurt and Berry Parfaits

Yield: 4 servings | **Prep time**: 10 min. | **Cook time**: 0 min.

Ingredients:

- 2 cups plain Greek yogurt (low-fat or full-fat based on dietary needs)
- 2 cups mixed berries (such as strawberries, blueberries, raspberries)
- 1/4 cup granola (look for a low-sugar, high-fiber option)
- 2 tablespoons honey or a sugar-free sweetener (adjust to taste)
- A few mint leaves for garnish (optional)

Directions:

1. In four glasses, layer 1/4 cup of Greek yogurt at the bottom.
2. Add a layer of mixed berries on top of the yogurt.
3. Sprinkle a tablespoon of granola over the berries.
4. Repeat the layers until the ingredients are used up, finishing with a layer of berries on top.
5. Drizzle a little honey or sugar-free sweetener over the berries and garnish with mint leaves if using.
6. Serve immediately or refrigerate until ready to serve.

Nutritional Information (per serving): 150 calories, 10g protein, 20g carbohydrates, 2g fat, 3g fiber, 5mg cholesterol, 50mg sodium, 200mg potassium

Lemon Ricotta Cake with Almond Flour

Yield: 6 servings | **Prep time**: 15 minutes | **Cook time**: 40 minutes

Ingredients:
- 2 cups almond flour
- 3/4 cup granulated sweetener suitable for diabetics (e.g., erythritol)
- 2 teaspoons baking powder
- 4 large eggs, separated
- 1 cup ricotta cheese
- Zest of 2 lemons
- Juice of 1 lemon
- 1 teaspoon vanilla extract
- A pinch of salt

Directions:
1. Preheat the oven to 350°F (175°C). Line a 9-inch springform pan with parchment paper and grease the sides.
2. In a bowl, mix almond flour, sweetener, and baking powder.
3. In another bowl, whisk together egg yolks, ricotta, lemon zest, lemon juice, and vanilla extract until smooth.
4. Gradually incorporate the dry ingredients into the wet mixture until just combined.
5. In a separate bowl, beat egg whites with a pinch of salt until stiff peaks form. Gently fold the egg whites into the batter to keep the cake light and airy.
6. Pour the batter into the prepared pan and bake for 40 minutes, or until a toothpick inserted into the center comes out clean.
7. Let cool before serving. Optionally, garnish with powdered sweetener and additional lemon zest.

Nutritional Information *(per serving): 300 calories, 8g protein, 30g carbohydrates, 18g fat, 3g fiber, 80mg cholesterol, 200mg sodium, 250mg potassium.*

Almond Flour Chocolate Chip Cookies

Yield: 12 servings | **Prep time**: 15 min. | **Cook time**: 12 min.

Ingredients:

- 2 cups almond flour
- 1/2 cup erythritol (or another sugar substitute)
- 1 teaspoon baking powder
- 1/4 teaspoon salt
- 1/3 cup unsalted butter, melted
- 1 large egg
- 1 teaspoon vanilla extract
- 1/2 cup sugar-free chocolate chips

Directions:

1. Preheat your oven to 350°F (175°C). Line a baking sheet with parchment paper.
2. In a large bowl, combine almond flour, erythritol, baking powder, and salt.
3. Stir in melted butter, egg, and vanilla extract until the dough comes together.
4. Fold in the chocolate chips.
5. Scoop tablespoon-sized balls of dough onto the prepared baking sheet. Press down slightly to flatten.
6. Bake for 12-15 minutes, or until the edges are golden brown.
7. Let cool on the baking sheet for 5 minutes before transferring to a wire rack to cool completely.

Nutritional Information (per serving): 150 calories, 4g protein, 6g carbohydrates, 13g fat, 2g fiber, 20mg cholesterol, 50 mg sodium, 30mg potassium.

Coconut Milk Panna Cotta with Berry Compote

Yield: 4 servings | **Prep time**: 20 min. | **Cook time**: 4 hours

Ingredients:

- For Panna Cotta:
- 2 cups canned coconut milk
- 1/4 cup sweetener (erythritol or monk fruit for a low-carb option)
- 1 teaspoon vanilla extract
- 2 1/2 teaspoons unflavored gelatin powder
- For Berry Compote:
- 2 cups mixed berries (fresh or frozen)
- 1/4 cup sweetener (as above)
- 1 teaspoon lemon juice

Directions:

1. In a small bowl, sprinkle gelatin over 1/4 cup cold water. Let stand for 5 minutes to soften.
2. Heat coconut milk and sweetener in a saucepan over medium heat, but do not boil. Add softened gelatin and stir until completely dissolved. Remove from heat, stir in vanilla extract, and pour into serving dishes.0000
3. Chill the panna cotta in the refrigerator for at least 4 hours or until set.
4. For the compote, combine berries, sweetener, and lemon juice in a saucepan over medium heat. Cook until berries are soft and the sauce thickens slightly, about 10 minutes. Cool before serving over panna cotta.

Nutritional Information (per serving): 250 calories, 2g protein, 18g carbohydrates, 20g fat, 1g fiber, 0mg cholesterol, 15mg sodium, 200mg potassium

Avocado Chocolate Mousse

Yield: 4 servings | **Prep time**: 15 min. | **Cook time**: 0 min.

Ingredients:

- 2 ripe avocados, peeled and pitted
- 1/4 cup unsweetened cocoa powder
- 1/4 cup sugar substitute (suitable for diabetics, like stevia or erythritol)
- 1/2 cup coconut milk (or almond milk for a lighter version)
- 1 teaspoon pure vanilla extract
- Pinch of salt
- Fresh berries for garnish (optional)

Directions:

1. In a blender or food processor, combine avocados, cocoa powder, sugar substitute, coconut milk, vanilla extract, and a pinch of salt. Blend until smooth and creamy.
2. Taste and adjust sweetness, adding a little more sugar substitute if needed.
3. Divide the mousse into serving dishes and refrigerate for at least 1 hour to set. This improves the mousse's texture.
4. Serve chilled, garnished with fresh berries if desired.

Nutritional Information (per serving): 250 calories, 4g protein, 15g carbohydrates, 20g fat, 7g fiber, 0mg cholesterol, 50 mg sodium, 500mg potassium.

Baked Apple Slices with Cinnamon and Nutmeg

Yield: 4 servings | **Prep time**: 10 min. | **Cook time**: 20 min.

Ingredients:

- 4 large apples, cored and sliced
- 1 teaspoon ground cinnamon
- 1/4 teaspoon ground nutmeg
- 2 tablespoons sugar substitute (suitable for baking and diabetics, like stevia or erythritol)
- 1/4 cup water

Directions:

1. Preheat your oven to 375°F (190°C). Arrange apple slices in a single layer in a baking dish.
2. In a small bowl, mix together the cinnamon, nutmeg, and sugar substitute. Sprinkle this mixture over the apple slices.
3. Pour water into the bottom of the baking dish. Cover with aluminum foil.
4. Bake in the preheated oven for 20 minutes or until the apples are soft.
5. Serve warm as a dessert or a side dish. Optionally, top with a dollop of Greek yogurt or a sugar-free whipped cream for an extra treat.

Nutritional Information (per serving): 95 calories, 1g protein, 25g carbohydrates, 0g fat, 2g fiber, 0mg cholesterol, 2mg sodium, 195mg potassium

Low-Carb Blueberry Cheesecake

Ingredients:

For the crust:
- 1.5 cups almond flour
- 1/4 cup melted unsalted butter
- 1 tablespoon erythritol (or another low-carb sweetener)

For the filling:
- 16 ounces cream cheese, softened
- 1/2 cup erythritol (or another low-carb sweetener)
- 2 large eggs
- 1 teaspoon vanilla extract
- 1/2 cup sour cream
- 1 cup fresh blueberries

For the topping (optional):
- 1/2 cup fresh blueberries
- A drizzle of sugar-free blueberry syrup

Yield: 6 servings | **Prep time**: 15 minutes | **Cook time**: 55 minutes

Directions:

1. Preheat the oven to 350°F (175°C). Mix almond flour, melted butter, and erythritol in a bowl. Press the mixture into the bottom of a 9-inch springform pan to form the crust. Bake for 10 minutes. Remove from oven and cool.
2. In a large mixing bowl, beat the softened cream cheese and erythritol until smooth. Add eggs one at a time, beating after each addition. Mix in vanilla extract and sour cream. Gently fold in 1 cup of blueberries.
3. Pour the filling over the cooled crust and smooth the top with a spatula. Bake for 35 minutes or until the center is just set. Turn off the oven, open the oven door slightly, and let the cheesecake cool inside for 1 hour to prevent cracking.
4. Chill the cheesecake in the refrigerator for at least 4 hours, preferably overnight.
5. Before serving, top with additional fresh blueberries and a drizzle of sugar-free blueberry syrup if desired.

Nutritional Information (per serving): 320 calories, 9g protein, 12g carbohydrates, 28 fat, 4g fiber, 120mg cholesterol, 200mg sodium, 180mg potassium.

Dark Chocolate and Walnut Brownies

Ingredients:

- 1 cup almond flour
- 3/4 cup granulated erythritol (or another low-carb sweetener)
- 1/2 cup unsweetened dark cocoa powder
- 1/2 cup unsalted butter, melted
- 2 large eggs, room temperature
- 1 tsp vanilla extract
- 1/2 tsp baking powder
- 1/4 tsp salt
- 1/2 cup chopped walnuts
- 1/4 cup dark chocolate chips (sugar-free, if available)

Yield: 6 servings | **Prep time**: 15 minutes | **Cook time**: 25 minutes

Directions:

1. Preheat your oven to 350°F (175°C). Line an 8-inch square baking pan with parchment paper.
2. In a large bowl, mix almond flour, erythritol, cocoa powder, baking powder, and salt.
3. Stir in melted butter, eggs, and vanilla extract until well combined.
4. Fold in chopped walnuts and dark chocolate chips.
5. Spread the batter evenly in the prepared baking pan.
6. Bake in the preheated oven for about 25 minutes or until a toothpick inserted into the center comes out with a few moist crumbs.
7. Let the brownies cool in the pan before slicing and serving.

Nutritional Information (per serving): 250 calories, 8g protein, 20g carbohydrates, 18g fat, 5g fiber, 80mg cholesterol, 200mg sodium, 300mg potassium.

Keto Lemon Bars

Ingredients:

For the crust:
- 1 1/2 cups almond flour
- 1/4 cup coconut flour
- 1/3 cup erythritol or other keto-friendly sweetener
- 1/2 cup unsalted butter, melted

For the filling:
- 4 large eggs
- 1 cup erythritol or other keto-friendly sweetener
- 1/2 cup fresh lemon juice
- Zest of 2 lemons
- 1/4 cup almond flour for thickening

Yield: 6 servings | **Prep time**: 20 minutes | **Cook time**: 25 minutes

Directions:

1. Preheat oven to 350°F. Line an 8x8-inch baking dish with parchment paper.
2. Combine almond flour, coconut flour, and erythritol for the crust. Mix in melted butter until a dough forms. Press into the bottom of the prepared dish.
3. Bake for 10-12 minutes until slightly golden.
4. Whisk together eggs, erythritol, lemon juice, and lemon zest for the filling. Stir in almond flour Pour over the baked crust.
5. Bake for 15-20 minutes until filling is set. Cool completely before slicing into bars.

Nutritional Information *(per serving): 300 calories, 8g protein, 10g carbohydrates, 25 fat, 5g fiber, 120m cholesterol, 200mg sodium, 100mg potassium.*

Raspberry Sorbet with Fresh Mint

Yield: 4 servings | **Prep time**: 15 min. | **Cook time**: 0 min.

Ingredients:

- 4 cups fresh raspberries (or frozen, thawed if fresh is not available)
- 1/4 cup fresh mint leaves, more for garnish
- 2 tablespoons lemon juice
- 1/4 cup erythritol or another low-carb sweetener, adjust to taste
- 1/2 cup water

Directions:

1. In a blender, combine raspberries, mint leaves, lemon juice, erythritol, and water. Blend until smooth.
2. Pass the mixture through a fine-mesh sieve to remove seeds, pressing with a spatula to extract as much liquid as possible.
3. Pour the strained mixture into an ice cream maker and churn according to the manufacturer's instructions, usually about 20-30 minutes.
4. Transfer the sorbet to a freezer-safe container and freeze until firm, about 2-3 hours.
5. Serve garnished with fresh mint leaves.

Nutritional Information (per serving): 80 calories, 1g protein, 18g carbohydrates, 1g fat, 8g fiber, 0mg cholesterol, 5 mg sodium, 200mg potassium.

Chia Seed Pudding with Coconut and Mango

Yield: 4 servings | **Prep time**: 15 min. | **Cook time**: 0 min.

Ingredients:

- 1/4 cup chia seeds
- 1 cup unsweetened coconut milk
- 1/2 cup diced mango
- 1 tablespoon shredded coconut
- 1 tablespoon sugar-free maple syrup or sweetener of choice
- 1/2 teaspoon vanilla extract

Directions:

1. In a bowl, combine chia seeds and coconut milk. Stir thoroughly to combine.
2. Mix in sugar-free maple syrup and vanilla extract.
3. Cover and refrigerate for at least 2 hours or overnight until it achieves a pudding-like consistency.
4. When ready to serve, stir the pudding, top with diced mango and shredded coconut.
5. Serve chilled.

Nutritional Information (per serving): 150 calories, 3g protein, 15g carbohydrates, 8g fat, 5g fiber, 0mg cholesterol, 50mg sodium, 200mg potassium

Sugar-Free Lemon Meringue Tart

Ingredients:

For the crust:
- 1 1/2 cups almond flour
- 1/4 cup butter, melted
- 1 tablespoon erythritol

For the filling:
- 1/2 cup lemon juice (about 2-3 lemons)
- 1 tablespoon lemon zest
- 1/2 cup erythritol
- 3 eggs (yolks and whites separated)
- 4 tablespoons butter

For the meringue:
- 3 egg whites
- 1/4 teaspoon cream of tartar
- 1/4 cup erythritol

Yield: 6 servings | **Prep time**: 30 minutes | **Cook time**: 20 minutes

Directions:

1. **Prepare the crust:** Preheat the oven to 350°F (175°C). Combine almond flour, melted butter, and erythritol in a bowl. Press the mixture into a 9-inch tart pan, forming an even layer. Bake for 10 minutes, then cool.
2. **Make the filling:** In a saucepan over medium heat, whisk together lemon juice, lemon zest, erythritol, and egg yolks. Add butter and cook, stirring constantly until the mixture thickens. Pour into the cooled crust.
3. **Create the meringue:** Beat egg whites and cream of tartar in a clean bowl until soft peaks form. Gradually add erythritol, continuing to beat until stiff peaks form. Spread the meringue over the filling, creating peaks with a spoon.
4. **Bake the tart:** Return the tart to the oven and bake for 10 minutes, or until the meringue is golden. Let cool before serving.

Nutritional Information (per serving): 320 calories, 10g protein, 4g carbohydrates, 28g fat, 4g fiber, 125mg cholesterol, 150mg sodium, 100mg potassium.

Avocado Cilantro Lime Dressing

Yield: 4 servings | **Prep time**: 10 min. | **Cook time**: 0 min.

Ingredients:

- 1 ripe avocado, peeled and pitted
- 1/4 cup fresh cilantro leaves
- Juice of 2 limes
- 1/4 cup olive oil
- 2 garlic cloves, minced
- Salt and pepper, to taste
- Water, as needed for consistency

(Ideal for drizzling over grilled chicken salads, taco salads, as a dip for fresh veggies, as a topping for fish tacos, or as a creamy dressing for southwestern-style quinoa bowls.)

Directions:

1. In a blender or food processor, combine the avocado, cilantro, lime juice, olive oil, and garlic. Blend until smooth.
2. If the dressing is too thick, add water a tablespoon at a time until you reach the desired consistency.
3. Season with salt and pepper to taste. Blend again to mix.
4. Serve immediately or store in an airtight container in the refrigerator for up to 2 days. Stir well before using if the dressing has thickened in the fridge.

Sugar-Free Tomato Basil Marinara

Yield: 4 servings | **Prep time**: 15 min. | **Cook time**: 30 min.

Ingredients:

- 2 tablespoons olive oil
- 1 small onion, finely chopped
- 2 garlic cloves, minced
- 1 (28-ounce) can of no-sugar-added crushed tomatoes
- 2 tablespoons chopped fresh basil
- 1 teaspoon dried oregano
- Salt and pepper to taste
- A pinch of erythritol or another sugar substitute, optional

(Ideal for serving with whole wheat or gluten-free pasta, as a base for vegetable lasagna, as a sauce for chicken parmesan, as a dip for baked mozzarella sticks, or as a topping for homemade pizza).

Directions:

1. In a large skillet over medium heat, warm the olive oil. Add the onion and garlic, sautéing until soft and translucent, about 5 minutes.
2. Pour in the crushed tomatoes, basil, oregano, salt, and pepper. If desired, add a pinch of erythritol or another sugar substitute to enhance the sauce's natural sweetness.
3. Reduce the heat to low and simmer the sauce for 20-25 minutes, stirring occasionally.
4. Taste and adjust the seasoning if necessary. Use immediately over your favorite low-carb pasta substitute or cool and store in an airtight container in the refrigerator.

Smoky Chipotle Aioli (Sugar-Free)

Yield: 4 servings | **Prep time**: 5 min. | **Cook time**: 0 min.

Ingredients:
- 1 cup mayonnaise (sugar-free)
- 2 chipotle peppers in adobo sauce, finely chopped
- 1 clove garlic, minced
- 1 tablespoon lemon juice
- 1/2 teaspoon smoked paprika
- 1/4 teaspoon salt

(Ideal for burgers, sandwiches, grilled chicken, and as a dip for fries or sweet potato wedges).

Directions:

1. In a small bowl, combine the mayonnaise, chipotle peppers, minced garlic, lemon juice, smoked paprika, and salt. Mix thoroughly until all ingredients are well incorporated.
2. Taste and adjust the seasoning if necessary, adding more salt or lemon juice according to your preference.
3. Let the aioli sit for a few minutes to allow the flavors to meld together. Serve immediately or store in the refrigerator in an airtight container for up to a week.

Fresh Mint Chutney with Yogurt

Yield: 4 servings | **Prep time**: 10 min. | **Cook time**: 0 min.

Ingredients:
- 1 cup packed fresh mint leaves
- 1 cup yogurt (preferably Greek for thickness)
- 1 tablespoon lemon juice
- 1 clove garlic
- 1 medium green chili, deseeded (adjust to taste)
- 1/2 teaspoon salt

(Ideal for Indian samosas, tandoori meats, as a spread in wraps, and with grilled vegetables).

Directions:

1. Wash the mint leaves thoroughly and pat them dry.
2. In a blender or food processor, combine the mint leaves, yogurt, lemon juice, garlic, green chili, and salt. Blend until smooth.
3. Taste the chutney and adjust the seasoning if necessary, adding more salt or lemon juice to your preference.
4. Serve immediately or refrigerate in an airtight container for up to 3 days. Stir well before serving.

Almond Butter Satay Sauce

Yield: 6 servings | **Prep time**: 10 min. | **Cook time**: 5 min.

Ingredients:
- 1/2 cup almond butter
- 1/4 cup reduced-sodium soy sauce
- 1/4 cup water
- 2 tablespoons lime juice
- 1 tablespoon erythritol or a suitable sugar substitute
- 1 clove garlic, minced
- 1 teaspoon grated ginger
- 1/4 teaspoon crushed red pepper flakes (adjust to taste)

(Ideal for chicken skewers, stir-fried noodles, spring rolls, and grilled vegetables).

Directions:

1. In a small saucepan, combine almond butter, soy sauce, water, and lime juice. Stir over medium heat until well combined.
2. Add erythritol, minced garlic, grated ginger, and red pepper flakes. Whisk continuously until the sauce is smooth and begins to thicken slightly, about 3-5 minutes.
3. Remove from heat and let it cool. Adjust seasoning according to taste.
4. Serve as a dipping sauce with grilled meats or vegetables, or use it as a dressing for salads.

Balsamic and Olive Oil Vinaigrette

Yield: 4 servings | **Prep time**: 5 min. | **Cook time**: 0 min.

Ingredients:
- 1/4 cup balsamic vinegar
- 3/4 cup extra virgin olive oil
- 1 teaspoon Dijon mustard
- 1 clove garlic, minced
- Salt and pepper to taste
- Optional: herbs such as basil or thyme

(Ideal for mixed green salads, as a marinade for chicken or vegetables, and drizzled over roasted potatoes).

Directions:

1. In a small bowl, whisk together the balsamic vinegar, Dijon mustard, and minced garlic.
2. Gradually add the olive oil, whisking constantly, until the mixture is well combined.
3. Season with salt and pepper to taste. Add herbs if desired.
4. Store in an airtight container in the refrigerator. Shake well before serving.

Creamy Greek Yogurt Caesar Dressing

Yield: 4 servings | **Prep time**: 5 min. | **Cook time**: 0 min.

Ingredients:

- 2/3 cup Greek yogurt
- 1/4 cup grated Parmesan cheese
- 1 tablespoon olive oil
- 1 tablespoon lemon juice
- 1 teaspoon anchovy paste (or finely minced anchovies)
- 2 teaspoons Dijon mustard
- 1 clove garlic, minced
- 1 teaspoon Worcestershire sauce
- Salt and pepper to taste

(Ideal for Caesar salads, as a dip for crudités, spread on sandwiches, and over grilled chicken).

Directions:

1. In a bowl, combine the Greek yogurt, grated Parmesan cheese, olive oil, lemon juice, anchovy paste, Dijon mustard, minced garlic, and Worcestershire sauce. Whisk until smooth and well combined.
2. Taste and adjust the seasoning with salt and pepper according to your preference.
3. The dressing can be served immediately or stored in the refrigerator in an airtight container for up to 3 days. Stir well before serving.

Lemon Tahini Dressing

Yield: 4 servings | **Prep time**: 5 min. | **Cook time**: 0 min.

Ingredients:

- 1/2 cup tahini
- 1/4 cup lemon juice (approximately 2 lemons)
- 2 tablespoons olive oil
- 1 clove garlic, minced
- 1/2 teaspoon sea salt
- 1/4 teaspoon black pepper
- 2 to 4 tablespoons water (to achieve desired consistency)

(Ideal for kale salads, as a sauce for falafel, drizzled over roasted vegetables, and as a dip for pita bread).

Directions:

1. In a medium bowl, whisk together tahini, lemon juice, olive oil, minced garlic, sea salt, and black pepper until well combined.
2. Gradually add water, one tablespoon at a time, until the dressing reaches your preferred consistency. It should be smooth and pourable.
3. Taste and adjust seasoning if necessary. If it's too thick, add a little more water. If you prefer it tangier, add a bit more lemon juice.

Raspberry Vinaigrette with Stevia

Yield: 4 servings | **Prep time**: 5 min. | **Cook time**: 0 min.

Ingredients:
- 3/4 cup fresh raspberries
- 1/4 cup olive oil
- 2 tablespoons white balsamic vinegar
- 1 packet stevia (or to taste)
- 1 tablespoon Dijon mustard
- 1/2 teaspoon salt
- A pinch of black pepper

(Ideal for spinach salads, mixed with fruit salads, drizzled over grilled salmon, and as a marinade for chicken).

Directions:

1. In a blender or food processor, combine the raspberries, olive oil, white balsamic vinegar, stevia, Dijon mustard, salt, and black pepper. Blend until smooth.
2. Taste the vinaigrette and adjust the sweetness or seasoning if necessary. For a thinner consistency, you can add a little water and blend again.
3. Serve immediately over your favorite salad greens or store in the refrigerator in an airtight container for up to 5 days.

Sugar-Free Cranberry Sauce

Yield: 4 servings | **Prep time**: 5 min. | **Cook time**: 15 min.

Ingredients:
- 3 cups fresh cranberries
- 1/2 cup water
- 1 packet stevia (or to taste, equivalent to 1 cup sugar sweetness)
- Zest of 1 orange

Ideal for Thanksgiving turkey, as a spread on sandwiches, with roasted chicken, and as a topping for yogurt or oatmeal.

Directions:

1. In a medium saucepan, combine cranberries, water, and stevia. Bring to a boil over medium-high heat, then reduce to a simmer.
2. Add the orange zest to the saucepan. Continue to simmer, stirring occasionally, until the cranberries have burst and the sauce has thickened, about 10-15 minutes.
3. Remove from heat and allow the sauce to cool. It will continue to thicken as it cools. Serve chilled or at room temperature.

30-Day Meal Plan

Day	Breakfast	Lunch	Dinner	Snack
Day 1	Quinoa Berry Delight with Almond Milk	Chicken and Vegetable Soup with Herbs	Pork Tenderloin with Apple Cider Vinegar Glaze	Mini Bell Pepper Nachos
Day 2	Sunrise Symphony: Steel-Cut Oats with Cinnamon and Flaxseed	Vegetable Lentil Soup with Kale	Duck Breast with Orange and Balsamic Reduction	Caprese Skewers with Balsamic Reduction
Day 3	Ricotta and Raspberry Stuffed Crepes	Spicy Tomato and Bell Pepper Soup	Grilled Tilapia with Mango Salsa	Cucumber Hummus Bites
Day 4	Whole Grain Avocado Toast with Cherry Tomatoes	Butternut Squash and Carrot Soup	Grilled Lamb Chops with Mint Pesto	Turkey and Spinach Roll-Ups
Day 5	Greek Yogurt with Mixed Berries and Nuts	Miso Soup with Tofu and Seaweed	Spicy Garlic Lime Shrimp	Eggplant Pizza Bites
Day 6	Tropical Chia Delight	Grilled Portobello Mushrooms with Quinoa Salad	Chicken Alfredo with Shirataki Noodle	Vegetable Spring Rolls with Peanut Dipping Sauce
Day 7	Savory Spinach and Mushroom Egg Scramble	Split Pea Soup with Ham	Beef and Vegetable Kebabs with Yogurt Tahini Sauce	Zucchini Fritters with Yogurt-Dill Sauce
Day 8	Turkey Bacon and Egg Muffin Cups	Mushroom and Barley Soup	Chicken Parmesan over Zucchini Noodles	Zucchini Fritters with Yogurt-Dill Sauce
Day 9	Vegetable and Hummus Breakfast Burritos	Turkey and White Bean Chili	Crab Cakes with Avocado Aioli (Using Almond Flour)	Smoked Salmon and Cream Cheese Cucumber Bites
Day 10	Low-Carb Blueberry Muffins	Chicken and Vegetable Soup with Herbs	Spiced Rubbed Pork Chops with Grilled Peaches	Greek Yogurt and Berry Parfaits
Day 11	Green Power Protein Smoothie	Vegetable Lentil Soup with Kale	Tuna Nicoise Salad	Mini Bell Pepper Nachos

Day 12	Mediterranean Sunrise Muffins	Spicy Tomato and Bell Pepper Soup	Oven-Baked Chicken Fajitas	Caprese Skewers with Balsamic Reduction
Day 13	Cottage Cheese Delight with Sliced Peaches and Pumpkin Seed	Butternut Squash and Carrot Soup	Stuffed Peppers with Ground Beef and Cauliflower Rice	Cucumber Hummus Bites
Day 14	Savory Mushroom and Zucchini Frittata	Miso Soup with Tofu and Seaweed	Chicken Piccata with Capers and Spinach	Turkey and Spinach Roll-Ups
Day 15	Quinoa Berry Delight with Almond Milk	Gazpacho	Balsamic Glazed Steak Rolls Filled with Vegetables	Eggplant Pizza Bites
Day 16	Sunrise Symphony: Steel-Cut Oats with Cinnamon and Flaxseed	Split Pea Soup with Ham	Grilled Salmon with Lemon Dill Sauce	Vegetable Spring Rolls with Peanut Dipping Sauce
Day 17	Ricotta and Raspberry Stuffed Crepes	Mushroom and Barley Soup	Beef and Broccoli Stir-Fry	Zucchini Fritters with Yogurt-Dill Sauce
Day 18	Whole Grain Avocado Toast with Cherry Tomatoes	Turkey and White Bean Chili	Moroccan Chicken Tagine with Olives and Lemons	Zucchini Fritters with Yogurt-Dill Sauce
Day 19	Greek Yogurt with Mixed Berries and Nuts	Moroccan Stew with Chickpeas and Vegetables	Seafood Paella with Cauliflower Rice	Smoked Salmon and Cream Cheese Cucumber Bites
Day 20	Tropical Chia Delight	Vegetable Lentil Soup with Kale	Slow Cooker Pulled Pork with Sugar-Free BBQ Sauc	Greek Yogurt and Berry Parfaits
Day 21	Savory Spinach and Mushroom Egg Scramble	Spicy Tomato and Bell Pepper Soup	Buffalo Chicken Lettuce Wraps	Mini Bell Pepper Nachos
Day 22	Turkey Bacon and Egg Muffin Cups	Butternut Squash and Carrot Soup	Baked Cod with Tomato and Basil	Caprese Skewers with Balsamic Reduction
Day 23	Vegetable and Hummus Breakfast Burritos	Miso Soup with Tofu and Seaweed	Turkey Meatloaf with Sun-dried Tomatoes and Feta	Cucumber Hummus Bites

Day 24	Low-Carb Blueberry Muffins	Vegan Jambalaya with Brown Rice	Meatballs in a Tomato and Herb Sauce with Zucchini Noodles	Turkey and Spinach Roll-Ups
Day 25	Green Power Protein Smoothie	Split Pea Soup with Ham	Grilled Chicken Breast with Herbs and Lemon	Eggplant Pizza Bites
Day 26	Mediterranean Sunrise Muffins	Mushroom and Barley Soup	Shrimp and Broccoli Stir-Fry with Garlic Sauce	Vegetable Spring Rolls with Peanut Dipping Sauce
Day 27	Cottage Cheese Delight with Sliced Peaches and Pumpkin Seed	Turkey and White Bean Chili	Beef Stir-Fry with Broccoli and Bell Peppers	Zucchini Fritters with Yogurt-Dill Sauce
Day 28	Savory Mushroom and Zucchini Frittata	Chicken and Vegetable Soup with Herbs	Turkey Meatballs in a Tomato Basil Sauce	Zucchini Fritters with Yogurt-Dill Sauce
Day 29	Quinoa Berry Delight with Almond Milk	Vegetable Lentil Soup with Kale	Low-Carb Meatloaf with Ground Turkey and Bell Peppers	Smoked Salmon and Cream Cheese Cucumber Bites
Day 30	Sunrise Symphony: Steel-Cut Oats with Cinnamon and Flaxseed	Spicy Tomato and Bell Pepper Soup	Mussels in a White Wine Tomato Broth	Greek Yogurt and Berry Parfaits

Friendly reminder: While we've included the nutritional values for the dishes in our book, please note these are estimates. For precise nutritional information, calculate based on the specific brands and quantities of ingredients you use.

Happy cooking!

Dear readers, if you found joy and value in this book, we kindly ask you to share your thoughts with a review on Amazon. Your insights are incredibly important to us and greatly assist future readers in discovering this work. We deeply appreciate your support and the time you take to share your experience

Made in United States
Orlando, FL
17 September 2024

51590016R10057